BRAIN SCRAPS

Pendra J. King

I dedicate this book to my parents and two brothers who have gone before me. I believe I'll see them again someday. I'm just trying not to rush it.

Oscar C. King (Oz)
Marilyn C. King (Mickey, Mick, Ma)
Tyler P. King (Ti-pi)
Timothy C. King (Tim, Mort!)

CONTENTS

FOREWORD

When I was young, my mother instilled the love of reading in me. We always had books in the house, and she encouraged reading whenever possible. As I grew older, I saw the pleasure she derived not only from reading, but also from writing. I picked up that habit from her at an early age and kept notebooks of ideas, conversations with others, and adventures I'd had or wanted to have. It's been fun going through these old scribblings and watching myself grow into the 60-year-old woman before you. This book is a compilation of stories I've been collecting for decades. A few stories will make you laugh. Others will make you cry. There might be a couple that offer some good advice for you. And maybe one or two will make you raise an eyebrow and think . . . "Can that really be?" If anything in this book gives you reason to pause and ponder, then I'm happy. Enjoy.

ACKNOWLEDGEMENTS

In many books I've read, I've seen a page or two, maybe three, of acknowledgements by the author. I always laughed and thought that's a lot of people to thank for writing one book. And then I wrote this book. NOW I get it! Although an author may write the book alone, he or she has so much input from others that it would be a crime to leave them out of the picture. I believe in giving credit where credit's due. In no particular order, here's a list of people to whom I owe my deepest gratitude:

Thank you, Lisa Winters, for proofreading my manuscript and putting it all together in proper form for publishing. This book would not have been possible without your hard work and extreme patience in dealing with this computer-challenged dinosaur! You're the best and I can't thank you enough.

With all my heart I thank my brother-from-another-mother, Jeffrey Becksted for his encouragement and unwavering support in this endeavor.

My most sincere appreciation goes out to my good friends Katy Collette and Marcelene (Marcy) Smutz for their never ending enthusiasm. There were times when I just didn't think I could pull it all together and they convinced me (thankfully) that I was wrong. A special nod to Marcy for Rocky. Yo.

To my sister Mary Anne Swenie, I thank you for believing in me and for reminding me I'm the captain of my ship.

Sometimes you don't know where you'll find the energy or creative ability to complete a goal. Then you look around and see others achieving magnificent feats and you think to yourself, "Man, if he can do THAT, surely I can do THIS!" And that's exactly what Paul Cirillo has done for me. Paul is an ultra-marathon man. Seriously. He thinks nothing of running a 100-mile race. On his laid-back race days, he may do "just" a 50-miler. As I sit in my comfy leather chair in my living room, I'll get online and watch his race tracker. I can follow Paul mile for mile as he does these incredible races. Too many times I told myself I couldn't complete this book. Almost on cue, Paul would post another race he was doing. That would snap me out of my "can't" mentality and push me into that "HELL YES!" zone. Paul, my most humble thanks. You ARE a machine!

When I first put the idea of writing this book out there among friends, they were all so upbeat and happy for me.

Seeing as this would be my first step into the publishing world, I wanted to test drive a few of my stories. To Alicia Mere and Roger LaShomb, I say thank you for reading my work and for your positive feedback. Your insight has been most helpful. I'm glad I could make you chuckle, cry, or raise an eyebrow!

Thank you, John A. Stubbe IV, for your heartfelt encouragement and support. And thanks for your input on one of my essays. Thank you, Arno and Tori Lippassaar, for the use of your serene cottage where I relaxed and completed so much work on this book.

There are so many others to whom I've mentioned this project and have received nothing but positive words and kindness. I'd love to list everyone, but I'd run out of room for my stories! You know who you are. You know you've been the wind in my sails when I needed the extra push. There aren't enough ways to say thank you for all the support, encouragement, and pure love I've received from you. From the deepest pocket of my plucky little heart, I thank you.

THE WEIGHT OF
THE BASKET

What a great Outdoorsman show! Booths stuffed with gear for hiking, hunting, camping, and any other activity involving nature were there. Fantastic vendors showing the latest and greatest in clothing and gadgets that you just HAD to have. I wandered through the arena, elbow to elbow, in a sea of like-minded fresh air enthusiasts. Don't you dare try to turn around and go back to that booth you just passed. You'll feel like a salmon swimming upstream.

I spent a good portion of the afternoon talking with the salespeople, owners of stores and shops, and product representatives who had answers for every question I asked. Seeing their faces light up as they explained how a certain gizmo worked or how you could wear a garment four different ways was entertaining as well as enlightening. I purchased a few things for my jaunts in the woods. I'm not a hard-core hiker or mountain climber, and at the time, I didn't hunt, so I didn't need any special equipment. Still, it was fun to look. And of course, they sometimes gave out freebies.

At about 3:45 p.m. the crowd started thinning out and an announcement was made that the show would be closing for the day at 4:00 p.m. but would be opening again tomorrow at 9:00 a.m. The announcer wished everyone a pleasant evening and said he hoped we'd be back tomorrow, and to please bring our friends. I was slowly inching my way toward the exit, trying to see a few more displays in the last row. That's when an elderly gentleman caught my eye.

He wore a soft, dark blue denim shirt and faded jeans. His face was deeply wrinkled and reminded me of freshly plowed fields–the rows of sod overturned one after another. His gray hair was pulled back into a long ponytail that reached between his shoulder blades. His untamed white eyebrows sat above his chocolate brown eyes that twinkled as I approached.

On his table sat ten pack baskets of various shapes and sizes. Some were tall and wide, like laundry hampers. Others were short and narrow. They were all beautifully woven with various shades of brown, tan, and reddish reeds. I stopped and said hello to the man seated behind the table. His face lit up. He began to tell me about his hand-woven baskets. He made them himself from cattails and other swamp grasses. He handed me a business card with his name, email, and phone number on it. I'm embarrassed to say I couldn't pronounce his name because he was a Native American and had a traditional first name. I sheepishly looked at him and introduced myself. He saw me studying his card and gave a little chuckle. "Call me Sam. It's easier." My relief must have been written all over my face because he laughed again.

Sam proceeded to tell me the process of collecting the reeds, keeping the best ones, discarding the ones with blemishes, cracks, or any rot on them. "You want a uniform basket. You want the pattern to be pleasing to the eye. You have to make it sturdy, so it won't fall apart. It has to be light so once you get all your stuff in it, it can be carried comfortably."

I nodded understandingly and said that I'd taken a few walks in the woods with my backpack that was too heavy. I confessed I have a tendency to overpack and then I'm miserable as I'm slogging along the trail. I whined about how I'd even given myself some bruises and raw spots on my shoulders and hips from carrying way too much stuff that I never even needed or used on my outing.

Sam nodded solemnly and asked me if I'd like to sit with him until his daughter showed up to take him home. Oh boy. Had I just lucked into what I was hoping would be another good story? Yes. Yes, I had.

Sam showed me each basket. One by one, he went over how the weaving was done, and why it was done that way. Strength, durability, and ease of use were the main priorities. Then he looked at me and said, "Pack baskets are like your heart. Do you know what I mean by that?"

"No, I'm not really sure. But I'm all ears if you want to tell me," I said.

He reached for the biggest basket on his table. He pulled it onto the floor between our chairs.

"Look at how big this basket is. You can put food in here. You can put a sleeping bag in here, too. You could tuck in clothes and even a little tent. Lots of room. If you pack it right, you can carry everything you need. No wasted room."

I nodded.

He continued. "When you pack your basket, you only need to take what's necessary for your trip. It's good to be prepared, but if you take extra things, they just weigh you down. They burden you. You'll get tired more easily, your body will hurt, and you won't be very happy. You told me a few minutes ago that you always overpack, is that right?"

I nodded again and said, "Yes, I always take too much stuff thinking 'What if I need . . .' and then I end up not needing any of it. It takes some of the fun out of a short hike, but I worry too much about not having the right tools and gear."

Sam's wise eyes started shining again. "Your heart is just like your pack basket. If you carry too much in it, you'll be miserable. Do you worry too much about things you can't control?"

"Uh, yeah. I do."

"And do you replay past events in your head? Do you think of old conversations and what you should have or could have said?"

"Umm . . . yup."

"Are you holding old grudges against someone who probably doesn't even know you're still angry?"

Damn. He had me nailed. I swear I'd never met this man before, but he was dissecting my mind and my personality like I was a lab rat. I thought maybe I had a window on my forehead, and he could see into my noggin to read my thoughts.

Sam lifted the big basket back onto the table then shifted in his chair to face me. "Why do you carry too much? It does you no good. It wears you out and drains your energy. Having a heavy heart will make your journey so much more difficult than if your heart is light. When your heart is heavy, you can't look up and see the sun. You're too tired to watch the stars. You won't have the energy to love the people who love you. The more unnecessary weight you carry in your heart, the less room you have in it for the beauty the world has to offer you."

3

I thought about this. I do carry grudges. I do think about things I screwed up or could have done better. I have regrets and embarrassments. Who doesn't? Could Sam be right? What good does it do me to hold onto these negative thoughts? These weights don't serve me. They give me emotional bruises and sore spots on my soul. Am I the only one who does this? Or does everyone carry too much?

"How do I lighten my pack basket . . . um . . . I mean heart?" I asked Sam. "How do I lighten my heart, so I have more room for the good stuff? I want the good stuff!"

Sam patted my hand and said, "You're already on your way if you can admit you're carrying too much. Look deep inside. Look at what isn't serving you. It'll take practice, but every day just picture yourself packing your basket. Picture yourself taking only what you need. If you feel something in your basket is too heavy, take it out. Set it aside. It'll still be there, but eventually it'll fade, and you won't see it or feel it anymore."

I smiled at Sam and told him I'm going to try that. I said I didn't know if I'd be successful or not, but it's worth a shot. And I'd try to lighten my real backpack too, because I was tired of the bruises and raw spots on my body.

I looked up and there was a woman about my age standing in front of the table. "You ready to head out, Dad?" she asked. Sam smiled and said yes. We all headed towards the door where we said good night.

The next day I went back and bought two of Sam's baskets. I bought one of his large ones and one medium-sized pack basket. I gave him my money and as he counted out my change, he said to me, "Now don't forget to take only what you need. The weight of the basket is all up to you."

I thanked Sam for the baskets and started heading for the door. I turned around, smiled, and said, "Thank you, Sam. For everything."

Sam gave me a short, knowing nod.

MA IN THE GROCERY STORE

Marilyn C. King. My mother. She always wanted that "C." in there. I don't know why, but that's where I picked up always putting my middle initial in my name. Pendra J. King. Does it make my name sound more complete? I don't know. It just feels right.

I could write several books on my mother: her antics, her gifts, her sense of humor. But for now, I'll just share stories about grocery shopping with her in the 1970's. We were just humble farm people. My father worked hard in the barn and fields to get that milk check once a month. He'd hand my mother a couple hundred dollars and expected her to stretch it like taffy at the state fair. Feeding eight mouths (and usually a few neighbors), on only a couple hundred dollars a month was a miracle only she could pull off.

Now remember, in the 1970's there was no internet, no Google, no email or Facebook. We lived in the country and there was no cable television service down our back country road. Even if there had been, we certainly couldn't have afforded it. Entertainment was up to us. Most of my siblings and I developed a twisted and warped sense of humor. The credit goes fully to my parents. They had different styles of humor, and we learned from both. I guess you could say we kids didn't have a choice or a chance. It's genetic.

One day I was helping Ma grocery shop in Massena. I was behind her, pushing the cart slowly while she sauntered ahead of me picking four cans off this shelf, six cans off that one, and not even looking around, but just reaching her hand down behind her to place the items into the cart. We had developed almost a dance. I knew enough to give her room and not run over her heel and make her bleed. (That's another story. I didn't do it.) My timing was perfected so she didn't have to chase me down or wait for me to catch up to her. I honestly don't remember her ever having to look back to find me in order to empty her hands.

Anyway, this one day we were both in a silly mood. I don't know why, but we were just giddy and snickering at inside jokes, picking on each other, mispronouncing words on purpose.

"Pendra, did you renew your 'prescription' to People magazine yet?"

"Yes, Ma, it was 'demandatory' that I do it this week."

As we drifted down one of the middle aisles of the supermarket listening to Fleetwood Mac on the store's speaker system, my mother was doing her usual grab-and-drop. For some reason, I halted to look at a new item on a shelf. Something about the packaging had caught my eye so I stopped, picked it up, and started reading what it was. In this moment, a woman of about fiftyish passed me on the left and ended up closing in on my mother. This woman's movement by me was enough to snap me out of my product curiosity. What happened next is etched in my memory forever.

Ma was about forty-two years old at that time. Standing at a whopping five-feet-two inches and weighing in at about a hundred and thirty pounds, she wasn't a beast. She was dressed in clean, presentable clothing. Her hair was neat, and she was as presentable as any other housewife would be. As I mentioned, she had a great sense of humor. She was not easily intimidated or offended. She could get a little "colorful" now and then. I think sometimes it's called bawdy. Other times it's called raunchy. That day I hit the jackpot.

I stood behind our grocery cart and before I could say anything, before I could holler forward the fifteen feet or so Ma had put between us, I saw her pick up a long, firm, glossily wrapped stick of pepperoni from one of those barrels sitting in the aisle. She held it near the bottom with her left hand and began to STROKE the length of it with her right and getting ready to turn around to make me laugh. She had felt the presence of the grocery cart right there behind her as it should be, so why wouldn't she think it was me? It wasn't. She slowly turned, erotically stroking this long pepperoni stick, licking her lips, twitching her eyebrows up and down, and flitting her eyes, and in the sexiest voice she could muster she said, "HERE'S A NICE

ONE FOR YOU, PENDRA!"

There was almost a cleanup in aisle five that day. I was hanging onto the handle of the cart and my knees were buckling. I was laughing so hard and couldn't even breathe. I was trying so hard to not wet my pants. My mother instantly surveyed the situation and she started cracking up. That is, as soon as she stopped giving Mr. Pepperoni his two dollars' worth of attention. The best part was watching the interloper stand there between us in utter and complete shock and horror. The look on her face was priceless. Also, it kind of made me feel sorry for her husband on some level. She gave a loud "HUHHHHHNNNHHH!" of disgust. At that moment my mother and I locked eyes. We both lost it again. The disgusted woman pushed her cart out of that aisle so fast that I swear there are still burn-out marks on the floor. Tears were streaming down both of our faces as we clung to the cart for dear life. Ma threw the pepperoni stick in the cart. She was invested by then. She may have even felt an obligation toward it at that point.

We regained our composure and continued with the grocery shopping. That whole scene only took about ten seconds, but it was pure gold. Probably the best ten seconds of my life.

To this day, when I pass by a barrel of pepperoni sticks, I whisper, "Hi, Ma" and I hear her say, "HERE'S A NICE ONE FOR YOU, PENDRA!" I always smile.

NO CABLE TV

We didn't have cable tv. No video games, no electronics, no mini-bikes or dune buggies. Nope. We had puzzles, board games, a basketball, a baseball, and a couple of bats. I'd say we were typical farm kids for that generation.

One humid summer night my father could see that all of us kids were sort of restless. He knew just what to do. "Get your shoes on," was all he said, but we noticed that gleam in his eye and that smirk on his face. My mother just looked up at him from the book she was reading and didn't even bother to ask.

We followed Oscar to the barn where he grabbed an empty burlap grain sack and filled it with loose hay. He then tied a piece of baling twine around the neck of it, so it stayed closed. We were all befuddled. What on earth was he up to now? He then snagged a handful of used baling twine from a nail. I know every farmer has twine hanging from several nails on their barn walls. I think that's a law.

Like little ducklings, the six of us made our way to the old farm truck and jumped in the back. Oscar tossed the burlap sack and the twine in the back with us. It was just about dark, but he still wouldn't give us any inkling of what we were going to do. We drove down the road, took a right, took a left, then another right. We ended up on a long stretch of road that was flanked by cornfields on either side. My father pulled into one of the fields where the tractors had made a path. He killed the lights and told us to get out of the truck.

Six pairs of feet hit the dirt. Oscar flipped the tailgate down and grabbed the sack of hay. He then tied a piece of baling twine to the one holding the bag closed. Then he tied several more pieces of twine until he had about thirty feet attached to the twine on the neck of the bag. Still no clue as to what we were doing. He handed the bag and rope to my brother and said to all of us, "Follow me!"

Down the dusty tractor lane we went toward the road. Along the way, he snapped off about four ears of corn and handed them to us younger kids. We were giggling but had no idea why. We just knew we were about to do something mischievous and couldn't wait.

When we made it to the road, Oscar looked left and right, and the coast was clear. He told us to put an ear of corn just barely on the side of the road right there, and then pointed to another spot about two feet from that ear. "Put another one there."

We did the same thing with the other ears of corn, but down the road a little further. Then he took the sack from my brother and carefully placed it, so the twine side was facing the cornfield. "Everybody in the cornfield!" he stage-whispered to us.

We ran into the corn and watched as our father joined us, but he was carefully laying the baling twine behind him. It wasn't long before a car came zooming along. It went past the bag but then hit the brakes. As soon as the brake lights came on, my father started pulling the string and running deeper into the corn. We saw what was happening and all felt a rush of excitement and panic, but in the best way possible! The car was turned around and heading back to pick up what LOOKED like a free bag of sweet corn that must have fallen off someone's truck, right? The car slowly came back. We all hunkered down in the tall stalks of corn, stifling giggles and nearly wetting ourselves. The car went by the loose ears of corn just knowing that bag was there somewhere. We watched eagerly as the car drove by us, slowly inching forward looking for their freebie. When the vehicle had gone way too far looking for what they knew had to be there, that's when my father dashed out and placed the bag in the original spot. Watching the taillights, we saw the car turn around again. It was heading back toward us, creeping at a snail's pace now. Damn it, they know they saw a bag. They weren't imagining it. AHA! There it is! The car was put in park, the driver and passenger jumped out and just as they were about to claim their free prize, the bag was suddenly jerked out of their reach and went flying into the cornfield! Oscar snapped the baling twine and was hauling the feedbag deeper into the cornfield. "RUN! RUN!" All six of us kids were running in our own rows, doubled over laughing at the people on the road.

"HEY, YOU SONSABITCHES!! YOU BASTARDS! WE'LL GET YOU FOR THIS!! THIS ISN'T FUNNY, YOU ASSHOLES! WE KNOW WHO YOU ARE AND WHERE YOU LIVE AND WE'RE TELLING YOUR PARENTS!!"

Trying to stifle giggles from six kids is impossible. My father knew this. He also knew the people in the car wouldn't chase the unknowns in a cornfield. We were safe.

We did this a few more times and all with the same results. Giggles. Obscenities yelled at us. More giggles. Finally, we loaded back up in the truck and headed home. We ran into the kitchen all vying for the opportunity to tell Ma what happened. Six kids panting and yelling about the bag and the corn and the people who called us bad names. My mother looked up at my father and tried to give him that "What are you teaching our children?" face, but she couldn't do it. She had us all repeat our escapade several times and laughed at each rendition.

Now THAT'S good parenting.

REINCARNATION?

"I wasn't dreaming. I know what dreams are. I've had them since I was a little kid, for crying out loud. And I wasn't drunk or stoned. This was NOT a dream."

Tim's eyes were serious. They didn't have that usual twinkle in them when he was telling a tall tale or trying to pull a fast one. Tim was twenty-nine years old and had been on his own since leaving the Army at twenty-two. He'd moved around for his job but always kept in touch when he was on the road. Our face-to-face visits were rare, but I cherished them when they happened. We sat at my kitchen table having iced tea and he was the one who brought up the subject of reincarnation.

"Do you believe in it?" he asked.

I gave it a thought then replied, "I'm not sure. I know there's something strange about déjà vu and that feeling of being familiar with a place or situation. Is that what you mean?"

"No. I mean have you ever FELT like you were someone else? Someone not of this time, of this era?"

This was a deep conversation coming from my brother who just liked to work, party, go back to work to earn more money to party, and so on. Tim was intelligent and a thinker, but I never knew him to take life TOO seriously.

"What prompted this? You said it wasn't a dream, so what was it?" My curiosity had been aroused and I wanted to know what, exactly, had turned my little brother into such a serious dude.

Tim stared out my kitchen window at the horses in the pasture next door. Quietly and slowly, he told me about an experience that obviously shook him to the core. "I was getting ready to mow the lawn and as I was pouring gas into the mower, I sort of froze for a minute. Hell, it might have been more than a minute. I don't know. It was like in the movies when everything stops, and you can hear the main character's heart beating in his chest. I could hear MY heart beating in my chest. I felt my breathing slow down, even though I was getting kind of scared. I thought maybe I was having a heart attack or something. But I didn't have any chest tightness or stabbing pains going down my arm. I was fine except I felt in limbo. Then I remembered looking down at my shirt and instead of the white t-shirt I'd put on that morning, I saw a uniform. It wasn't my U.S. Army uniform. It was a German military uniform just like in the World War Two movies and books. It was a grayish-green color, and the buttons were different. I had a swastika on my arm. When I looked down, even my shoes were different, they were these old-looking boots that I'd never wear, especially to mow the lawn."

He went into more detail about what he was wearing for that frozen moment in time, and it was clear to me he'd had an interesting experience. Then he went on to tell me he'd had other dream-like moments, but he knew he was awake. He described in detail how one morning he was getting up, ready to start his day. As he lay there in bed going over his to-do list, he could "hear and see" in his mind a full conversation with another man in the same kind of uniform. However, they were speaking German. Fluently.

"Pendra, all the German I ever learned was from watching *Hogan's Heroes* on television when we were kids. I don't know anything more than what Sgt. Shultz could mutter!" Tim kept shaking his head as he tried to make sense of all of it. "So, do you think I'm going crazy, or is this reincarnation?" His puzzled face told me he wanted answers. Or at least a reasonable explanation.

I let out a little sigh and told him I didn't think he wasn't crazy. I admitted I had a confession of my own and went on to tell him about my trip to Europe four years before. "We stopped at a castle in Austria. It was gorgeous! We paid our admission fee and joined a group of about a dozen people and followed our guide through the building. I can't explain it, but as marvelous as the place was, I felt a little let down because it was already familiar to me. I knew what was around every corner. I knew where every staircase led and what we'd find in the next room. Nothing was a surprise for me, and I didn't get that 'ooh-ahh' moment when something cool came into view. I had never read a book about this castle and had never seen it on television, but I swear I knew that place inside and out. I've never told anyone about it because I didn't want to get locked up in the nuthouse! Ever since that trip, I've had what I thought were dreams where I was speaking another language. I can't tell you what language it is, but I can tell you what it isn't. Strange!"

We sat there silently. Finally, Tim spoke. "So you believe in reincarnation then? For real?"

I nodded. "I do believe we've lived past lives. I'm not so sure about the idea of learning from our mistakes and getting better and better as we go on. If that was the case, wouldn't everyone in the world be nicer by now? Wouldn't we all have gotten it right after a few repeats?"

Tim thought about that and agreed. We chatted a little while longer, then he had to get going. I asked him to keep me up to date if he had any more *Twilight Zone* episodes with his German counterparts. He said he would and asked me to do the same if I ever figured out what language I was speaking when I had my moments.

Our conversation kept replaying in my head. I decided to ask a few other people about their thoughts and ideas on reincarnation. Not the ones who think they'll come back as a daisy or a bumble bee. No, I wanted to know if anyone remembered past lives and did they also get flashes of memories?

At the time, Jeremy was a twenty-year-old college kid. He was straight from New York City, born and raised in Brooklyn, with the best damned accent ever. If you asked him about his accent, he'd look at you quizzically. "Whuuut ax-cent?" he'd ask. Jeremy was a friend of a co-worker's daughter who was attending Potsdam State College. I asked him to meet me at a pizza shop and I'd buy him dinner. Yes, I baited him with food. I knew he'd say yes like any young, starving college student would. Sitting in a local pizza parlor, we chatted about his studies, how cold the winters up here are, and anything else that popped into our heads. I asked him about his travels, and he dropped his head sadly and admitted that, other than going back to the city for the scheduled college breaks, he hadn't been anywhere in his whole life.

I then told Jeremy I was doing a little research on reincarnation. His eyes lit up. My friend had told me about Jeremy's experiences and that's why I wanted to meet him. He didn't say a word, and I could tell he was waiting for a prompt from me. He's a city boy, so I thought a direct approach would be fine. "Jeremy, do you believe in reincarnation? Have you ever thought you had a past life?"

"OH, HELL YES!" was his quick reply. I smiled and asked him to expound on that.

"I can tell you for a FACT that I used to live and work in Mexico! I used to work with cattle. Lots and lots of cattle. Pendra, the closest I've ever been to a real cow is at the steakhouse when I order a prime rib. But I can tell you how to handle them. I feel I could ride a horse easily enough, and best of all, I can speak Spanish! I mean real Spanish, not just my neighborhood lingo."

Jeremy excitedly told me he asked for cowboy boots for Christmas one year and his grandfather gave him a pair. "I've never felt so comfortable and at home in a pair of boots as I do in those." He told me about the chaps he used to wear, the wide-brimmed hat, the bandana around his neck. In his previous life, of course, not in Brooklyn.

I laughed and asked, "Are you sure you haven't watched too many spaghetti westerns?"

His dark eyes met mine and I quickly apologized. Jeremy gave too many descriptive details about life in Mexico, about herding and taking care of cattle, for it to be just a dream or some subconscious influence from a movie.

We finished our meal. I paid the check and asked the waitress to wrap the leftovers for Jeremy. He walked me to my car and asked me, "Do you believe me? Do you believe I was a true vaquero many years ago?"

I told him I believed him with all my heart. I thanked him for his honesty and candor. We hugged and, as I got into my car, I could see his grateful smile almost as if his deepest thoughts had been validated as he walked back toward his dorm.

This next reincarnated person came as a total surprise to me. I was attending a high school basketball game with a couple of friends who had kids playing that night. I sat on the hard bleachers watching the game and cheering for our team. At one point I looked down and to my right and sitting three rows ahead of me was another friend and her young daughter. Kristi was no more than six years old at the time. I gave her a little finger wiggle wave and she giggled and waved back. I could see her tugging on her mom's shirt and asking her something. Her mom turned around, saw me, smiled, and then nodded. Kristi came up to my level and plopped down beside me. "How are you, Kristi?" I asked.

"Pretty good, but I'm bored," was her reply.

"It's almost half-time, so you can probably go get a snack from the concession stand. That'll help."

"Naw, I don't wanna. I wanna sit here with you."

This surprised me because, although I don't dislike children, I've never had that rapport with youngsters. I'm not a mom, just an aunt. I get along fine with little ones, but I don't have that natural ability with them.

This didn't seem to bother Kristi. She accepted me as is, which can be best described as awkward with kids. We sat on the sturdy bleachers watching the first half of the game wind down. I could hear Kristi singing a song, but I wasn't familiar with it. I was sure it was something from a Disney movie, but I wouldn't have bet my life on it. At half-time I looked down at Kristi and said, "You sing very well! Will you be joining chorus or the school plays when you get older?"

"Yes, I will." And just like that, it was a done deal in her mind. Her little head snapped up and down to the affirmative. "I used to sing a lot. Back when I was fat."

I laughed. "Kristi, I've been friends with your mom for years, and I've known you since you were born! You've never been fat!"

"No, I mean BEFORE! When I was fat BEFORE," she insisted.

"Before what? You're only six years old and I've known you for all of those years."

The look on her face was pure exasperation. She went on to explain what I didn't know. "When I was fat, I used to sing in a really big building! It had lots and lots of seats and they were all squishy like the velvet dresses I used to wear. If you looked up, there were seats up high so they could look down and watch me sing! I used to look at the people up there so they wouldn't get lonely."

What she was describing to me sounded like an opera singer. I encouraged her to go on with her story. Part of me was hoping this was an accidental meeting of another reincarnated person. The other part told me she'd just watched a movie and was inserting herself into the plot.

"Having a big belly made me sing really good! Everyone

could hear me even all the way to the back doors!"

She was standing on the bleacher and pushing her tiny belly out as far as she could. Her arms reached out in a wide, palms-up position as her tiny voice sang out. "OOOOOHHHH AAAHHHHHHH! TRRRRRRRR!" She rolled her r's on the last part as expertly as any opera singer I'd ever seen on television. She then giggled and said good-bye to me when she saw her mother had a dish of nachos with cheese.

After the game when we were all tromping down the bleachers, I caught up with her mom. I told her about my conversation with Kristi and about how well she sang when she was fat. Her mother looked at me, shook her head, and said, "She insists she used to be big, and she used to sing. We don't play opera in the house. I don't think she's ever seen an actual opera performance on tv. Where she gets her love of it is beyond us."

I shrugged my shoulders. "Hey, kids are full of surprises, right?"

In my mind, I want to believe she was an opera star many moons ago. I'm anxious to see if she ends up as one again in another ten years or so.

I could give you at least a dozen more stories about people I've talked to about reincarnation. Maybe another time. I'm sure you've felt something different now and then, something you just can't seem to put your finger on or explain. Or maybe you know someone who has so many details of another life, full of talents and skills that they don't possess right now. How can someone go into such vivid detail unless they were there?

Do we live again and again? Do we carry forward small bits of our previous lives with us? Maybe someday we'll have the answers. Maybe not. Oh, but what a ride in the meantime!

TOYS

This story is another true incident that happened a long time ago. 1997, to be exact.

When we were growing up on our small dairy farm on the outskirts of Brasher Falls, there were a couple of families that lived just down the road a piece from us. One of those families was the Becksteds. Herb and Barb had four kids. Their oldest, Jeffrey, was the same age as my little brother Tim. Jeff used to come down to our farm and hang out with us. Being the oldest of four kids, he didn't get the abuse of being the youngest, like Tim did. I think he kind of liked how we older kids would harass, abuse, and pick on him. He always took it well. Who knows, maybe he went home with a deeper appreciation for NOT being the baby of the family! Over the years, Jeff became a fixture in our home. He was my bonus little brother. In 1979, I graduated and moved out of the house. (Yes, that's what kids did back then. They either went to college, joined the military, or went into the workforce and moved into their own apartments or homes.) I'd still visit my folks and little brother about once a week, or whenever my work schedule allowed. I'd see Jeff now and then and it was fun to watch him grow up and make his way in this world.

Fast forward to 1997. Jeff was living and working in Texas. He was headhunted by a large company and had the opportunity to go to Japan and intern there for a while. This was so exciting! Not only for Jeff, but for his girlfriend Christine, and all of us here at home. We were all so proud of this young man who was going places. Literally!

Christine decided to throw Jeff a good-bye party with all of his friends down there in Texas in attendance. She contacted me, and also one of my sisters still in the area and asked if we'd like to go down to Texas for the weekend and surprise Jeff. HELL YES! She gave us plenty of time to make our travel plans. Imagine Jeff's face when he saw his sisters! Or as we used to say, "I'm his sister from another mister!" or "He's my brother from another mother!"

Personally, I was extremely proud of Jeff and excited for his new adventure. And yet . . . part of me felt bad for his girlfriend. She'd be home alone in Dallas for a long time. Was it a year? Oh sure, she'd fly over to Japan to visit Jeff a few times He'd probably make it back to Texas to see her now and then. But still, that's a long time to be apart from the one you love. It was then that I decided to buy a companion for Christine. You know, something that would keep her company on those lonely days and nights. What could be more appropriate than a rascally rabbit? Hmmm . . . some of you are thinking I bought Christine a cute little fuzzy bunny. You would be mistaken. "The Rabbit" was a popular toy back in the 90's. Many rabbits showed up at parties as gifts or jokes or a little bit of both. I'm sure you've figured out what this object is and how it's used!

I told my sister that I'd purchased this toy for Christine because I didn't want her to feel lonely while Jeff was in Japan. She rolled her eyes. Yes, I'm the "bad" sister. I'm the one with the dirty mind, the morbid sense of humor, and the inappropriate language at times. Not my fault. You've met my parents, haven't you? It's genetic!

Anyway, I wanted to make sure this precious little bunny was in working order before giving it to Christine. Oh, by the way, did I mention the party she was throwing for Jeff was at their local watering hole? And yes, this gift was going to be presented in front of all their friends. Perfect.

But I digress. Okay, so I put the batteries in the little control box that had a wire attached to the base of the bunny. There were two buttons on the control box. When I flipped the one on the right to the first "ON" position, the rabbit's ears would vibrate and twitch at a moderate rate of speed. If I pushed that button further up the box, the vibrations and twitching of the ears became more intense. They twitched better than a real rabbit's nose. Perfect! I slid that control button back down the side of the box to the "OFF" position. I then pushed the button on the left side of the box to the "ON" position. At the base of the bunny was a round area about the size of a big jawbreaker candy. This clear ball had hundreds of colored bb's in it. When I hit the "ON" button, a little agitator inside that ball moved the bb's around and around and around. GRRRRR! GRRRRR! GRRRRRRR! The see-through rubber ball was mixing up the colored bb's better than any KitchenAide ever could! I pushed the button further up the control box. GRRROWWWLLL! GRRROWWWLLLL! Those little colored bb's were spinning faster. The little arm inside was moving at a pretty good clip now and as I put my fingertip to the side of the little bb-infested dome, I was tickled. Quite literally! My fingertip was getting a massage AND I felt the vibrations. But this wasn't enough. I went back to the first button on the other side, and I let 'er rip. Both buttons at full speed ahead! I could have mixed cement with that baby! GRRRRR! GRRROWWWLLL! BUZZZZZZ! BUZZZZZZ! I was in tears laughing at how perfect this gift would be.

I shut everything down. I was very careful to push both control buttons to their "OFF" positions. I double checked both sides of the control box and then gently placed everything back in the plastic molded packaging. Everything fit perfectly snugly in the case and then I slid the case into the outer box. I grabbed the gift wrap and made a pretty package for Christine. (Did I say "package?")

My sister and I drove to the Syracuse airport on the morning of our departure. Full disclosure: I did tell my sister that Christine's gift was in the bottom of my duffel bag. She gave me one of "those" looks but also knew I didn't care. We pulled into the parking lot of the airport, grabbed our duffel bags, locked the car, and headed inside. Remember, this was 1997. It was long before any terrorists turned our world upside down. People still had a sense of humor back then, too. Or so I thought.

We went up the stairs and headed for the security checkpoint. My sister went through first. She tossed her bag onto the conveyor belt and stepped through the metal detector. The gentleman on the other side barely glanced at her and waved her to the right. She retrieved her bag and stepped aside. My turn. I gently placed my bag on the belt and stepped through the metal detector. That's when I heard the three women behind the x-ray screening area start to mumble. Then giggle. Then some serious talking was going on, but I couldn't hear what was being said. The belt stopped. I was holding up traffic behind me. They called to the male screener who had just waved my sister through, but he was holding his palm up for me to stop. I looked to my right. My sister was glaring at me. The corners of my mouth started twitching as I stifled a giggle. I knew I had nothing illegal in my bag. The security man walked around to the employee side of the x-ray machine, and he began to chastise the ladies working there for laughing. Obviously, this was NO LAUGHING MATTER! He quickly pulled me aside to a table next to the end of the conveyor belt. He snatched my bag and a look of absolute panic was on his face. His voice was high-pitched, and he spoke fast. "WHAT DO YOU HAVE IN HERE? DO YOU HAVE A MECHANICAL DEVICE?? WHAT ARE YOU TRYING TO TAKE ON BOARD THE AIRPLANE?!"

I was having the hardest time not laughing. I realized the man was only trying to do his job. I was trying to be respectful, but . . . I glanced to my left and the three women behind the machine were dying. They were trying not to crack up but weren't succeeding very well. I looked back at this man. And to be fair, he was of Indian descent. India-Indian, not Native American Indian. I guessed his culture does NOT permit women to own, let alone transport certain, ahem, "adult" toys.

I remained polite and calmly responded to his shrill questions. "Yes, sir. I do have a battery-operated item in my bag."

He practically screamed at me. "TAKE IT OUT!! TAKE IT OUT OF YOUR BAG RIGHT NOW!!"

I glanced to my right and I could see my sister looking for a way to crawl under the tile floor. A quick look behind me and a crowd of people had gathered on the pre-screening side and they were all craning their necks to see what could possibly cause such a stir. I unzipped my duffel bag and carefully pulled out my jeans, a couple of shirts, my toiletry bag, and then I reached down to pull out this beautifully gift-wrapped box. The only issue was . . . it was growling. The package was vibrating and growling. BZZZZZ! BZZZZ! GRRRROOOWWWWLLLL! Oh my. I was trying to hold my face straight, but I knew I wasn't succeeding. The ladies running the machine had gathered closer to the table now. The man reached out and violently yanked the gift from my hands and tore the paper off the front of the box. Through the window of the box, we could all see the rabbit's ears vibrating and twitching. The clear ball at the base with the colored bb's was grinding around and around. BZZZZZ! GRRROOOOWWWLLLLLL! The ladies appreciated it. The man did not.

My sister then nervously and loudly proclaimed, "IT'S A BRIDAL SHOWER GIFT!! IT'S A BRIDAL SHOWER GIFT!!"

I looked over at her as if to say, "What the hell are you talking about?" but the words didn't escape my lips. I was too shocked to see her bugged-out crazy eyes and honestly, I feared her body was about to explode!

The security man practically threw the box at me. He was thoroughly repulsed. He hollered at me to take the batteries out of that . . . that . . . THING!! I opened the box, slid the plastic molded part out, and took the batteries out of the control box. He then ordered me to take my stuff and get out of the area. I stood there trying to put my clothes back in my bag, but he was yelling at me to GO! GO! GO!! I scooped up my open duffel bag with my right arm, grabbed my clothes with my left, picked up Christine's bunny, and carried all of it down the ramp toward the gate area. About fifty feet away from the security checkpoint, I set everything on the floor and began to repack my bag. If looks could kill, I'd have been a dead woman. My sister looked down at me in pure hatred. "NEVER in my life have I EVER been so embarrassed and humiliated!" she hissed. I was on my knees stuffing clothing into my bag and was literally in tears from laughing so hard. The whole episode was just too much. Nobody was hurt. Nobody missed a flight. Nothing illegal happened. So, what was the big deal?

The people who had been in line behind us were walking past us to get to the gate area. A few ladies smirked. A couple of men outright smiled. Several people walked by and totally ignored me, probably hoping I wasn't sitting next to them on their flight.

We made it to our gate and had some time to wait. "I am NEVER going to travel with YOU again!" she spat out. I can still hear her words in my head. And for a while, that was true. She never forgave me for that stunt, but she did end up traveling with me a few more times over the next number of years. And yes, she checked my bag before entering the airport. Every. Single. Time.

Now here's an interesting tidbit: I know I had the control box buttons set to "OFF" on both switches. I know I placed it in the molded case, and then into the outer box. And wrapped it with gift wrap. Then, how did the controller knobs slide to the "ON" position while in the box? I would have noticed the buzzing after I wrapped the box, or when I was packing it. My theory is our brother Tyler did it. Tyler was killed in 1985, but he had a great sense of humor. I've often wondered if this was a little gag played by Tyler's ghost. That's the only explanation I can come up with for what happened at the Syracuse airport in 1997.

OUR HAUNTED MANSION

We referred to it as The Mansion because it was the biggest house in which we'd ever lived. The grand Victorian stood majestically on two acres with sturdy oak and maple trees standing guard on the front lawn. There was a U-shaped driveway with the house on one side, and a large red barn on the other. Two long cedar hedges outlined the back of the property's edge and served as a great place for games of hide-n-seek. There was a small brick structure near the house which was used as a smokehouse in the olden days. The sidewalk ran in a straight line from the back corner of the house and made a sharp right-hand turn to the entrance at the front. Just offset from the front sidewalk was a concrete post with a metal ring in it to tie your horse and a step next to it so you could enter or exit your carriage safely. The house was white, square, and solid. On the very top was a cupola which, in our young minds, is what really set this house apart from "regular" homes.

Stepping inside you first noticed the rooms were wrapped in exquisite woodwork. Parquet flooring in the front hallway, hardwood floors throughout, and strong, heavy wood trim on all the doors and windows just begged for polish. Large decorative plaster casts on the ceilings centered the hanging light fixtures. On the main floor there was a huge mudroom, kitchen, butler's pantry, laundry room, dining room, bathroom, study, and two living rooms which were separated by enormous sliding pocket doors that disappeared into the walls. This home was full of magic.

On the second floor we found seven generously sized bedrooms, each with its own closet. In the hallway was a stairway leading to the third floor which held the attic, and then a few more steps to the cupola. The attic was mostly open except for an interesting room that was built right in the middle of it. The room was approximately ten feet by twenty feet. It had one small window to look out into the rest of the attic, and one small door for the entry/exit. This room certainly raised a few questions. Questions that the eventual answers tended to make a person raise an eyebrow or two.

The cellar was huge and open enough that we could play and ride our bikes around down there during the winter. To say this house was perfect for a family of eight would be an understatement.

And then . . . things started happening.

On our first night in the mansion, my father had to work the evening shift at the Lipton factory, so he was gone. My mother was used to my father working one, two, and even sometimes three jobs to keep the family afloat. She was never nervous about spending the night without him. By 9:00 p.m. we kids were all tucked into our beds upstairs. Each one of us was excited to finally have our own room. No more double or triple bunking with other siblings. Ma finished picking up a few stray boxes downstairs then went into the double living room to relax for a little while before heading to bed herself. She sauntered through what she later dubbed the "kids' living room" into the formal living room and turned around to close the heavy sliding pocket doors. The very idea of having a NICE living room to sit and visit with guests was a dream to my mother. She stood there with the lights off, facing the front lawn, enjoying the glow cast from the streetlights into the curtainless room. She was finally living in a house that was big enough for everyone. Her mind was filled with possibilities that lay ahead. As she stood there, her heart was filled with gratitude and happiness. She and my father had been working so hard for this day. It was then that she suddenly felt and heard someone breathing heavily on the back of her neck. She mentally cursed herself for not turning on the lights as she had entered the living rooms. The lights from the street had been more than enough to move about the rooms without bumping into any furniture. Ma stood there silently, feeling the warm, moist air being breathed onto her skin. It sounded and felt threatening. Her heart pounding, she slowly raised her hands out to her sides and hoarsely whispered, "Please don't hurt me and don't hurt my kids. Take anything you want, but please don't hurt us." Her body was shaking, and her heart threatened to explode in her chest. Tears formed in her eyes, but she didn't dare make a move or a sound. With a crippling feeling this was her first and last night in our new home, her only thought was for her children. That's when she knew she had to do something, so she slowly turned around. She was ready to fight this person for the sake of her kids. As she turned, she saw nothing. Nobody. The streetlights were bright enough that she would have seen anyone in the room with her. The breathing had stopped, but nobody was there. The double doors were still closed. The door leading to the hallway was still shut. Ma ran to the light switch and flipped it on. A quick scan of the room showed no other person in there with her. She quickly ran upstairs to check on all of us. As we lay there sleeping, totally oblivious to the possible danger of an intruder, my mother silently but frantically searched each of our rooms. Nothing. She went downstairs, turned on every light, and searched the rest of the house. All the doors and windows were locked. Needless to say, she didn't sleep that night.

Ma didn't tell us about that incident until quite a while later. It wasn't until several other events had happened that she finally decided she'd better sit us all down and explain that our new home was "special" in certain ways. She wanted to give us a heads-up in case we started experiencing odd moments ourselves. I remember now how she left out any details that would have made us feel threatened.

During our four years at that house, all of us except my older brother experienced paranormal activity. It was common to walk through cold pockets in the house, even during the hottest of summer months. Occasionally we'd see a blue light, about the size of a basketball, floating around one of the rooms, then exit. A couple of us could smell various perfumes or other scents that just didn't fit with anyone in the house. We never heard the cliché of chains rattling, but we heard other noises.

I recall one of the funniest times was when a family friend came to visit and play cards with us. Bob Kleinhans was a Jehovah's Witness who happened to stop in one day and instead of converting my mother to his religion, he became her friend. They'd have friendly arguments about religion over cups of coffee and cigarettes. He was an older bachelor and once in a while my mother would invite him to stay for dinner. Hanging with a huge family was torturous fun for Bob. One evening we were all sitting around our large dining room table playing Hearts. Everyone was laughing and picking on each other as we always did. Bob had heard the stories about the odd happenings at the house but always laughed them off as my mother's overactive imagination. As we sat there waiting for Bob to deal the next hand, we heard a baby crying. The sound was wafting down the stairs from the second floor, or maybe the attic. Bob's eyes got a little bigger. "Baby?" he asked.

"Yes, Bob. That's the baby."

Bob looked across the table at my little brother who was about seven years old at the time. "I thought Tim was the baby of the family."

Bob was confused. Here sat my little brother and yet Bob had distinctly heard a baby's cry coming from upstairs. Then it happened again. The rest of us were picking up our cards and getting ready to play our hands. It was old hat to us by then. Bob listened for another minute or two, then looked at my mother. She winked at him and asked, "Believe us now?"

He was speechless. Still, the logical side of him had to investigate, so my mother took him upstairs. He fully expected to find a baby doll or maybe a tape recorder set up to prank him. Nothing like that could be found. However, when they entered the attic and walked toward the finished room up there, Bob suddenly stopped and stood still. He slowly turned around, his eyes bugging out of his head, and said, "That's enough. I believe you now." They went back downstairs, and we finished our game of Hearts.

My mother needed to know what was going on, so she dug into some local history books and talked to older people in the neighborhood. Turns out the house was built by a family by the name of Ostrander. The Ostranders were known for being brilliant people. They were a highly intelligent and successful family. However, several older folks remembered hearing from their parents that the Ostranders had a mentally challenged child, and they kept that child hidden away in the attic. They took care of him, of course, but back then a mentally or physically challenged child was an embarrassment, a shameful thing in any family. Nobody ever recalled actually seeing this boy, but there had been rumors. Back then you just didn't talk about those things. You kept them private and tended to them quietly.

It made sense as we noticed many of the strange sounds came from the attic area. The blue lights would float up the main staircase and through the door of the attic stairway. That finished room in the attic was large enough for a bed, dresser, and for a child to play with toys. It certainly made the story of the mentally challenged child believable.

Another scary incident was when my parents were at the kitchen table having coffee with their friends Jerry and Anna May. Their daughter Phyllis was a friend and classmate of my older sister. The girls were playing around upstairs in one of the extra bedrooms that we used for storage. As the adults were chatting downstairs, they suddenly heard the girls running in the room directly above them. The girls then came bounding down the back staircase, heading into the butler's pantry when my father could hear what he thought was my older brother chasing the girls. Well, that was not going to happen. My father didn't mind the kids having fun but chasing the girls down the stairs was not safe and definitely not funny. The girls were screaming (as teenage girls are wont to do) and as they hit the landing at the bottom of the stairs, my father jumped up from the table and headed toward the staircase. He could hear the heavy footsteps chasing the girls, so he was going to snag my brother by his shirt and whip him around to meet him face-to-face. My father gripped the doorcase with his right hand and swung his left arm forward to capture the culprit. Nothing. Nothing but air. My father looked up at the empty back staircase and there was nobody there. My sister and her friend were barely understandable as they told the four adults that something was chasing them through the back room and down the stairs. All of the adults had heard the footsteps of three people. My father immediately walked down the front hallway and went upstairs to my brother's room, which was at the opposite end of the house. Big brother was in his bedroom doing homework. He wasn't out of breath. Wasn't sweating. He had no idea what had just happened. It was obvious to my father that this was not a prank pulled by him. It was just another one of those things that happened in that house.

The folks and my sister agreed to keep this scary chase quiet. We younger kids were in the living room watching television and had no idea what had just taken place in the back stairway. The folks figured we didn't really need to know, so why scare us? It was one thing to feel cold pockets, hear a baby, or see blue lights flitting about, but it was totally off-putting to be chased by something that wasn't there.

About two weeks later I was in my bedroom and Ma called us kids down for supper. I started coming down the front stairway and I could hear someone behind me. I fully expected one of my brothers to mow over me on the way to the dinner table, so I turned around ready to laugh at whichever one it was. I turned and saw nothing, but still heard the footsteps. I kicked it up into high gear and ran down the rest of the stairs. The heavy footsteps were right behind me. I could tell they were NOT echoes of my own footfalls. I barely made the corner at the bottom and dashed down the hallway and into the kitchen screaming to my mother that something was chasing me. She held me tightly as I shook and babbled about the pounding footsteps following me. Ma glanced over at my father and my older sister then said, "Okay, we have something to tell you kids." And that's when they let us younger ones in on the previous stairway chase. My mother reassured us that although these odd occurrences were nerve-wracking, they were not harmful. We had come to terms with the weird stuff such as the lights and the baby crying, but how were we to handle getting chased? As far as I know, none of us were chased down the steps after my incident. Maybe the kid in the attic was just playing?

Many other weird happenings occurred at that house over the next few years. I'd like to say we got used to these eerie times, but we didn't. Some things were fine, but other things were disturbing. We were never physically harmed, just freaked out. In 1974, my parents decided to sell the house and move back to the North Country where they were both born and raised. We didn't move up here because that house was haunted. It was because that neighborhood was becoming a bit rough, and the folks knew the North Country was a much calmer and safer area to raise children.

A young couple without children bought the house from us. They were schoolteachers and a very likable couple. The wife jokingly asked if the house was haunted. My mother told her, "Yes, actually, it is." The lady laughed. My mother looked her right in the eye and said, "It really is." Then she told her a few of the things that had happened since we had lived there.

More laughing. My mother said, "Okay, here's our address in Brasher Falls. Please write to me in a month." Yeah, you can see where this is headed. In less than a month my mother received a long letter from the new owners of the mansion. The first line was an apology for laughing at Ma. The rest of the letter contained a list of experiences the couple had witnessed in the house already. Ma and the new owners exchanged letters for a while, but after a bit there really wasn't much to say, so the letters stopped. I often wonder how long that couple stayed in the house? I also wonder if that mentally challenged child will haunt that house forever? I hope he finds peace someday.

YES

It's so common now to pick up a magazine or read an article online that tells us it's all right to say NO. The power of NO is emphasized to the overworked, stressed, tired people of today. You don't want to go to that party? Say NO. You've already worked ten hours today and the boss asks if you can stay an extra hour? Say NO. Your child is begging you for a toy that he'll play with for one day then be bored? Say NO.

I admit the power of NO can be wildly intoxicating. It frees us to do more of what we want. It saves us money and time. NO can salvage your pride and it can keep you out of embarrassing situations. NO is wonderful! It's pragmatic. It's efficient. Learning to use the word NO is almost like a drug. The more you use it, the more you need it. You'll eventually start feeling comfortable incorporating this powerful word into your vocabulary. For most people, saying NO is difficult because we're taught to be helpful and obedient from the get-go. There are few times when NO has been acceptable without question, such as when we're kids, and our parents told us NO to smoking, drinking, drugs, and sex. We were told NO when we wanted to play in the street or jump from second story windows. NO can be a lifesaver!

It took me way too many years to master the art of NO. Even now, I sometimes hesitate to say NO when I really want to because I'm afraid of hurting feelings or disappointing someone. I'm getting better at it, and it's liberating, but it takes practice. My advice to younger people would be: Learn the art of NO early on and you'll be happier than if you didn't use that magic word. Caution: Use discretion. Don't NO every little thing because that makes you an impudent brat. In real life there are times when we must do things we don't want to do. It's called adulting. Get used to it.

On the flip side, I've learned to say YES much more often than before. Selfishly speaking, the YES answers usually benefit me, and sometimes others. I've finally reached a point in my life that I feel I deserve a little more kindness from myself. Instead of putting everyone else's wants and needs ahead of mine, as most women are trained to do, I've decided to say YES to the woman in the mirror. However, I have strict guidelines and rules when it comes to the use of this delicious YES. First, it can't hurt or short anyone else. I'm selfish, but not selfish enough to harm anyone else in the process. I've experienced a few people who don't have a problem with that but, personally, I do. Whenever I want something, desire to go somewhere or do something, my first question is: Will this take away from anyone else? If the answer is no, I go on to the next question. I'll then ask myself: Will this put me in physical, emotional, or psychological danger? No? Then please proceed to the next step: Will this devastate me financially? I don't mind spending my own money, but I don't want to flush it down the toilet. I worked too hard for too many years to lose it all on a whim. Will I use and enjoy this for more than a few days or weeks? Warning: A short attention span can cause serious YES remorse!

Those are the most important questions I ask myself before I say YES to something. Obviously, there are other queries that pop up depending on the situation, item, or person involved. I address those as they apply to the scenario. If I can't answer YES to all of these, then it's likely I'll tell myself no. I'd say 99.99% of the time I'm glad I stopped myself from saying YES too often. We're only human. It's so easy to get distracted or carried away.

I've noticed as I've aged, my YES answers are geared not so much towards material objects, but to more personal avenues. I've come to terms with the fact I'll never be a saint. Not even close. And yet, the older I get, the more value I place on having a good heart, good intentions, and good people in my life. Priorities do change as the years roll by. Here's an abridged version of my YES list:

1. I'm saying YES to more laughs. I've always loved a good joke, pun, or story. I want more of these, whether in print or verbal.

2. I'm saying YES to being kinder to myself. No more bitching

about a few extra pounds, scars, crooked teeth. Perfection is like beauty . . . in the eye of the beholder. And I'm holding myself to a more generous and loving standard these days.

3. I'm saying YES to taking better care of myself so I can live, laugh, and love longer!

4. I'm saying YES to more music and dancing, even if it's only in my kitchen while I'm cooking.

5. I'm saying YES to spending more time with animals. There's something soul enriching about being with animals. I've never heard anyone complaining as they walked away from a decent animal. I guarantee your spirit will be fed each time you dote on a critter.

6. I'm saying YES to hanging with people I truly enjoy. They fill my heart and I appreciate every moment with people who sincerely care about me.

7. I'm saying YES to being outside more, even in the buggy weather! It's a fact that being outside is good for you in every way.

8. I'm saying YES to creativity. Writing, drawing, painting, gardening, and a host of other outlets are fun and fulfilling.

9. I'm saying YES to new music, new food, new authors. What good is a mental buffet if you only take one small plate of what life has to offer?

10. I'm saying YES to desserts. Oh . . . wait . . . I've always said YES to desserts. I guess this one is just a confirmation YES.

11. I'm saying YES to letting things slide. When someone hurts my feelings or slights me in any way, I try not to get all spun up about it anymore. I tell myself they're obviously unhappy with themselves, otherwise they wouldn't be lashing out as they are. Their anger is not about me, it's about them; therefore, it's none of my business.

You can see what I'm getting at here. There's a time and place for every YES or NO answer. The trick is to use them wisely. Question yourself before you give your answer. Make up your own rules or stipulations, but keep a couple of basic ideas:

Don't hurt anyone else. Don't hurt yourself.

And that's pretty much how this book came about. I've always wanted to write a book and I finally said YES. Now stop and think of all the things you could be saying YES or NO to and how much happier your life will be. Don't go crazy denying everyone everything, and don't go wild accepting everything that comes your way. I'm just tossing it out there for you to think about for a bit.

IN THEIR SHOES

Life teaches us lessons in the oddest ways. We rely on our parents, teachers, and other adults to guide us (sometimes unwillingly) in our youth, but then we grow up and we're out on our own. We think we have all the answers and get a bit cocky now and then. Being young and full of piss and vinegar can make one feel immortal. Then there are times when we're given a gift, a surprise lesson that sticks with us for the rest of our lives. This story is one of those lessons I learned, and feel is a valuable one to pass along to you.

It was a stifling hot day in July, and I had to head into town to do some errands. Groceries to get, banking to do, hit the hardware store for a few items, and gas up the buggy. I'm one of those people who likes to do all my running around in one fell swoop. I grabbed my tote bags for my groceries, tossed them into the back of my car, and headed into town. I live just a few miles out of town and one of the ways I head into the big city of Massena is called the South Racquette River Road. The locals spell it that way, or "Racket," or even "Raquette" so whatever your pleasure is fine. As you're driving on this road, heading into the big city of Massena, there's a drop in the speed limit from 55-mph to 40-mph. Then, as you crest a small hill, there's another drop from 40-mph to 30-mph as you hit the village line.

I'd been traveling that road for many years, and it was habit by then to automatically slow down to 40-mph when I passed the Humane Society, then lighten up on the gas pedal as I topped the second hill to the village line where the 30-mph zone started. Often, I'd see a police car running radar at the bottom of the second hill, just before the stop sign. Now, I have nothing against the police doing their job, so don't even start on me. I appreciate them running radar because it's a good reminder for everyone to slow the hell down. My point here is, I'm cognizant

34

of the fact that if I'm stupid enough to ignore the clearly posted speed zone signs, then I'll get a well-deserved ticket. It's hard to blame someone else for your own stupidity, right?

On this errand day, as I was entering the 40-mph zone, a full-sized pickup truck came barreling up behind me. I was doing the speed limit already and it was a no-passing zone, so there wasn't anything I could do except keep driving straight. Less than a quarter of a mile ahead was the stop sign where that road intersects with Main Street. I looked in my rear-view mirror and the truck was so close to my back bumper I swore I was going to get tapped. I was now entering the 30-mph village speed limit zone, so I let off the gas and slowed down to the proper speed. Apparently, this didn't please the person in the big truck behind me. All I could see in my mirror was the grille and, to be honest, this kind of scared me. It was a bit of a *Mad Max* feeling.

As fate would have it, there was no police vehicle sitting at the bottom of that hill on that particular day; however, again, as fate would have it, there WAS a train shuffling down the tracks and that held everyone up not only on Main Street, but also the South Racquette where I was now stopped with this angry truck parked two inches from my bumper. I was the fifth car lined up behind the stop sign. I looked in my mirror and saw the line of vehicles behind me growing slowly. Nothing we can do but wait at this point, right? Just as I was checking out the line, the driver behind me started honking the horn and giving me the finger. I could see it was a woman and, although I'm not a lip reader, I could distinctly make out what she was calling me and where she wanted me to go. I'm also guessing what she was suggesting was not physically possible because I'm not that limber. I didn't think I had done anything wrong, so being the smart-ass that I am, I looked in my rear-view mirror, smiled, and blew her a kiss. I thought that was hilarious.

I was mistaken.

As I sat in my car mindlessly counting the railroad cars and checking out the talented artists' graffiti on them, some movement in my mirror caught my eye. The driver of the pickup truck that had been hovering on my bumper was exiting her vehicle and heading my way. Approaching me was a very tall and stout woman with anger written all over her face. She looked like she could have tossed my car out of the way if she'd wanted to and honestly, she looked like that just might have been her intention. She stood at least five-feet-ten inches tall and weighed at least two hundred and twenty pounds but all muscle. She wasn't flabby. Her light brown hair fell slightly below her muscled shoulders which were frighteningly visible as they bulged out of her tank top. I couldn't tell exactly how big her hands were because they were balled up into fists. Very large fists. My heart started pounding a little faster. Holy shit. This linebacker was going to smash my window, drag me out of my car, and beat me to a pulp. I was too close to the car ahead of me to turn around. This gal's truck was nearly touching my bumper, so I couldn't back up. I was trapped. I knew she was about to activate my dental plan and there was nothing I could do about it. I guess my sarcastic air kiss wasn't appreciated. It only took her about five steps to reach my vehicle. She slapped my window with her open palm and started screaming at me. Her face was red and contorted with rage. "WHAT THE FUCK IS YOUR PROBLEM, BITCH?! WHY THE HELL ARE YOU GOING SO GODDAMN SLOW? YOU DON'T OWN THE FUCKING ROAD, YOU STUPID ASSHOLE! OTHER PEOPLE USE THESE ROADS TOO, YOU FUCKING CUNT!" There was more, but you get the gist of it.

Wow. Okay, so she wasn't going to break the glass and perform a car birth with me as the auto baby. She just stood there yelling, flailing her meaty arms, kicking several small stones towards my car. I noticed a few people in front and behind me were watching this show just waiting to see how bloody it was going to get. I was kind of curious too and had a quick thought that I should have updated my will last week. The train was still plodding along slowly.

She wasn't going away, so I inched my window down just enough so she could hear me as I started to explain I travel this road often and there's usually a cop running radar down here and I didn't want to get a ticket. She wasn't listening. She flew into another flurry of obscenities hurled in my direction. I closed my window and stared straight ahead but kept her in view. Finally, after what seemed like an hour but was probably no more than two minutes, she returned to her truck.

And that's when something hit me. Something intangible yet so strong that I couldn't ignore it. I like to think we all have people watching over us and helping us through life. In that moment, I'm positive someone was sending me a message. I turned my car off, unbuckled my seatbelt, and opened my car door. I'm pretty sure the people in the other cars were wishing they'd brought a bucket of popcorn for this show. I slowly walked back to the truck where this woman was watching my every move. When I stopped at her vehicle, I tapped on the window very lightly with my index finger. The scowl on her face told me she wasn't done hating me yet, but she was staying in her truck, so I took that as a good sign that I'd live to see another day. She rolled her window all the way down, not a cowardly two inches like me. I looked her right in the eye and said, "I'm very sorry for being so slow as we were coming into town. I travel this road all the time and I can't tell you how many times I've seen the police writing tickets in the 40 and 30 zones. I realize now you're in a hurry and I'm sorry I held you up." Her face seemed to soften just a fraction. I went on. "I'm also sorry for being a smart-ass and blowing you a kiss in my mirror. That was totally uncalled for, and I was out of line. Sometimes I think I'm funny when I'm not, so I apologize for my rude behavior. I wanted to piss you off, but that was definitely childish and the wrong thing to do, so I'm sorry."

And that's when the tears started falling. The last thing I expected was for this mountain of a woman to slump forward and start bawling her eyes out. I stood there silently as she hung onto her steering wheel and cried. Big, chest-heaving sobs were emanating from this woman. After a moment, she regained her composure somewhat and looked at me. "I'm sorry too," she said. Then the rush of words and emotions spilled out of her window to me. "My dog just died this morning and I've had her for twelve years and she was my baby, and I don't know what I'm going to do without her!"

Now I was tearing up because I'm a mush when it comes to animals, and I've lost pets too. I know the pain, the total agony of losing a fur baby. My heart went out to this woman. I reached up and lightly placed my hand on hers and told her how sorry I was for her loss. And I meant it. Then I asked her if there was anything I could do. I asked her if she needed to just go sit somewhere and have a cup of coffee or anything. She placed her other hand over mine, sandwiching it between hers. She declined my offer but thanked me for asking. Again, she apologized for being such a wreck and for calling me such horrible names. I gave her a smile and told her I work with a lot of men, and if that's all she's got, she'd better step up her game. This made her laugh a little.

We looked ahead of us, and the train had finally ended, and the line of cars was moving. I gave her hand a squeeze and told her to take care and that I'd be thinking of her. She squeezed back and nodded at me.

I walked back to my car crying.

Lesson learned. We don't always know why people do the things they do. We don't always know the suffering they're going through at any moment. I'm just thankful that "somebody" told me to get out of my car and go talk to this gal. She may have received a moment of comfort from me, but she'll never know the valuable lesson she gave back. So, be kind. Be compassionate and forgiving. When someone is being a total dickhead to you, show a little mercy if you can. It's not always all about you. Take a minute to walk in their shoes.

RELATIONSHIP ADVICE FOR MEN

I've noticed a disturbing trend these past 10-15 years or so. It's the half-in half-out guy. I know there are plenty of women already nodding at this expression because they're living with this notion right now. They're wondering if they should quit wasting their time and get out now, or if they should hang in there and hope it'll turn into something more. Is your guy really all-in, or does he have one foot out the door?

I'm going to offer some tips for the men who are mature enough to see a woman's value and want to lock it down. Whether he's looking for a monogamous long-term relationship (no legal ties) or a definite marriage, here are some things every man can do to show a woman he's serious about her. And only her. Don't make her wonder if you're a half-and-half guy.

1.   Call her just to say hi. It's those once in a while, out of the blue calls just to say hello that mean so much to us. Don't call her ten times a day. Stalking is not sexy. Interest is. Let her know you thought of her when you passed by a garden today and saw her favorite flowers. Tell her you heard a song that reminded you of her. If you're in the grocery store, pick up her favorite snack food so, when she comes to your house, she'll have what she likes there.

2.   If you both agree you're in a monogamous relationship, take her out in public and introduce her to your friends as your girlfriend. If she's not just someone you picked up in a bar last night and took home for some boot-knockin', then give her the respect she deserves. Let people know she's important to you

and you care about her. When you don't introduce her to your circle of friends, you're disrespecting her and letting her know she really is NOT that important to you. Ouch.

3. Guys, never underestimate the power of touch. Can you touch her gently without heading straight for her boobs, butt, or crotch? If not, learn how to do that. Women love the soft touches on their shoulders, head, arms, waist. Warmly placing your hand on her back will make her smile. Non-sexual touching is a powerful form of intimacy. It shows you care for, love, and respect her.

4. When you give your woman a birthday card or a valentine, actually put her name on the top. Write some sweet, cute, mushy words of affection in it. Make sure to sign your name. Even if the card has a sentimental verse, a simple "This says how I feel" written in your handwriting will mean the world to her. And here's another piece of advice: you can give her cards all year long. Yes! You can even scribble short notes or draw a heart or smiley face and put them where she'll find them. Honestly, she will LOVE them. Written reminders that she means something to you are always appreciated.

5. It's really great when a man cooks for his woman. It's even better when he cleans up after making the meal. Take it all the way, buddy. Complete the mission. She'll show you how much she appreciates it.

6. If you're serious about this woman, use the words "we," "us," "our" in your normal conversations. If you see yourself with her long-term, then using these words will mean everything to her. When you speak in couple-ese, you're telling everyone you think she's special. She'll adore you for it.

7. Presents. Here's a warning: if she expects presents all the time–RUN! Seriously. If she's a user and expects you to give her gifts, always pay for dinners and movies, always take your vehicle everywhere, then smarten up and run. You have a gold digger on your hands and she's going to run you into the ground financially. I don't care how gorgeous she is, how envious all your buddies are when they see her with you. If she's a user who won't stand on her own two feet and contribute to the relationship, RUN. Now then, if she's the opposite and she treats

you to dinner once in a while, buys you a tank of gas when you're always using your car, or pops up with tickets to the gun show, then you're golden. Please feel free to leave her favorite candy bar in her lunch bag. Pick up a pretty bar of soap that's scented with her favorite smell. Bring home one rose. Or one carnation. Or whatever flower she loves. You don't have to go overboard. They sell bouquets in Walmart that are inexpensive and pretty. Five bucks will get you a lot of smiles. Do something silly. Send her a note or a card in the mail. Everyone loves getting real mail and not just bills. Does she love creamed corn, but you gag over it? Get a can and place it under her pillow. She'll be confused but she'll laugh and love it. Is she into art but you'd rather have a colonoscopy than go to an art show? Get two tickets and tell her they're for her and a girlfriend. Does she have a sidewalk or paved driveway? Grab some sidewalk chalk from your niece and draw a heart and put your initials in it. See what I'm getting at here? Small gestures once in a while are what will melt her. You don't have to do something every single day. She'll love it at first but then it'll be expected, and you certainly don't want her taking you for granted. Mix it up. Surprise her. Let her know you're thinking of her with small, silly, mushy displays of your love. Let her know she matters.

8.   If you've been dating seriously for six months or more and you know you want her around, ask her to leave a few things at your house. Some women are bold and will just tell you they're leaving a change of clothes and toiletries. Be careful of those women. Real women are respectful of your territory but would love it if you'd ASK them to leave a few things. You can do it by saying it's convenient for the nights she spends at your home. What you're really saying to her is you want part of her there even when she's not. You're telling her she's important enough to let her into your personal space. We women hold out for a long time hoping you'll be the one to do the asking. We wait for you to come up with what we need to hear. If you were totally ignorant of this fact, now you're not, so get on it.

9.   How well do you know this woman? Have you ever sat down over dinner or on the front porch and just talked about her ambitions? Her dreams? What was she like as a child? What was her family life all about and how did it shape her into who she is today? Do you know what her favorite color is? Why

won't she wear stripes? Who would she give her left arm to see live in concert? What authors does she read? What bothers her deep down? What makes her happy? Women want you to know them. We really aren't that hard to figure out. Just ask us. If she plays games or is too elusive, then she's hiding something. Don't ask her how many men she's been with, or what her girlfriends confide in her, or anything that's none of your business. Everyone has secrets that should stay with them and only them. If you really care about this lady, get to know her on a deeper level. Get invested in her soul. Learn all about her.

10.   Here's a biggie: women dig old-fashioned manners. Yes. Seriously, we do! When you're at a restaurant, help her out of her coat and hang it up or drape it over a chair. Pull her chair out as if you've always done it and will always do it. Open doors for her and as she's going through, feel free to place your hand ever so lightly on her back as you follow her through the doorway. Take off your hat while inside. Take off your hat when you're kissing her. No woman wants to get sliced by the visor of a hat when you lean in to kiss her. When you're waiting for her at a public place and she walks in, stand up and smile. Let her know you're eager to see her. Don't just sit there and wave her over to your table. I'll be the first to say it: some women have taken feminism too far and have ruined it for the rest of us. They've neutered good men and have made it impossible for them to be gentlemen. They've confused the hell out of the male species. Why would any man hold open a door for a woman these days? There's a 50/50 chance he'll be yelled at and taken down a few pegs for being a kind, decent, polite human being. I applaud those of you who still do the right thing. I, for one, will always appreciate a door opened for me and will always smile and say thank you. Manners matter.

11.   Here's a story I'm stealing from a good friend named John. He was dating a gal and he was pretty head over heels for her. One day while she was at work, he snagged her spare car keys and took her car back to his place. He washed it inside and out. Wiped down everything, cleaned all the glass, vacuumed, left it spotless. He returned it to her place of employment but, before he left, he put a red rose and a short, sweet note on the driver's seat for her to find. Oh. My. God. BEST gesture EVER. As he told me what he had done, I almost started crying. When a

man spends his valuable time to do something for you that you consider unpleasant . . . wow. Just wow. Out of the goodness of his heart, he did a task to show her he loved her. Men, please do these gestures because I guarantee she'll love them.

12.   Gents, take pictures of your woman. She'll put up a fuss or complain she doesn't have her hair done or makeup on but go ahead and take those pics but only for yourself. Don't take unflattering pictures of her then post them to social media. Take lots of pictures of the two of you together. Better yet, hand your phone to someone and ask them to take your picture as you wrap your arms around her. This shows her you're proud to be with her. You're not ashamed to be seen with her or to have people know you're a couple. Print out your favorite shots and put them on your fridge, your desk, or any place you (and others) will see them often.

13.   If she must go away for a few days for work or school, give her the surprise of a few groceries in her fridge when she gets home. The last thing anyone wants to do is go grocery shopping after traveling. If you know she's coming home on Wednesday morning, go over and shovel her driveway and sidewalks on Tuesday night. If she's gone for a week, feel free to mow and trim her lawn. Chances are, she won't ask you to do these things. If you tell her you'll take care of these chores while she's away, she'll say, "Oh, you don't have to." But deep down she's sighing and saying thank you. Tell her you'll water her plants, feed the goldfish, and pick up her mail. If she's uncomfortable with you doing that for her, she'll let you know.

That's enough to get you guys started. You don't have to do everything I mentioned above. Those were just seeds of ideas to get you started. Personalize your attention on the woman you know. If she's worth your time and you want her in your life, show her.

RELATIONSHIP ADVICE FOR WOMEN

Let's be fair. I've already given a few gems of advice for men, so now it's time for a few tidbits for the ladies. I've made more relationship mistakes than I can count, and in my eyes that makes me a good one to give advice. You know, that ol' "Do as I say, not as I do" treasure. This one is going to irk the hell out of the women's libbers everywhere, so if you're one of them, you might want to skip this chapter. Contrary to popular belief, you can be a feminine woman and still be all about equal opportunity.

1. Be a real woman. Don't try to outdo him in everything or anything just because you can. If he cooks you a decent meal, don't go overboard and put on a lavish gourmet meal just to show him you're better in the kitchen. Hey, he did a great job. Enjoy it. You like 4-wheeling? Great! Doesn't mean you have to go through deeper puddles or harsher terrain to prove you're tough like him. You can nail a 2x4? Excellent! But you don't have to show him the house you're building all by yourself. My point is, it's fine to be a strong and independent woman. You just don't have to neuter your man along the way. Let him help you with projects. Do things together without competing. The more you show him you don't need him, the more he'll realize you're right and walk away.

2. Accept his gifts with a smile, no matter how off the mark they may be. I'm totally guilty of not hiding my feelings over a couple of gifts that, honestly, I wondered what the hell made him think I'd like THAT. The very fact that he is giving you a gift is sweet. I know it's hard to smile and take something that may have you

shaking your head but be polite and thank him. You can take it home and stuff it in a drawer or re-gift it to someone he'll never see using or wearing that gift. By the same token, I've given gifts that were way off the mark and sometimes I've been told the truth–and felt bad about being in the dark. But, then again, if I'm that oblivious to my guy's tastes, that tells me I need to ask more questions and learn more about the dude. I don't think it's right to let your partner buy or make you things that just aren't "you." Nip this in the bud by talking and communicating what you like and what he likes. You'll save a lot of time, money, and feelings in the end. After a while, those gifts will be spot-on, and you won't have to fake it to spare his feelings. Until that day comes, smile and say thank you.

3.   Don't bitch about his family. He's known them longer than you have. He can see you're right about a lot of things, but because they're his blood, he can't openly agree with you. Remember, blood will always be thicker than water. You have a couple of choices: either keep quiet when it comes to his family or walk away. It's really that simple.

4.   Pull your fair share in the relationship. Don't use him. You don't necessarily have to match him dollar for dollar, or chore for chore, but don't put all the burden on him just because "He's the man." This isn't the 1950's anymore. You're not helpless. You're not a delicate little thing that can't lift a finger. Some days it's 50/50, other days it's more like 70/30. Still, if he's treating you right, he deserves to be respected and appreciated. Men respect women who are their partners, not their dependents.

5.   I've asked numerous men about their pet peeves when it comes to the women they love. Most of them prefaced their remarks with, "I love her to death, but . . . " and then the comments came. A LOT of comments. So, straight from the source, here are a few things that we're all guilty of, but maybe didn't realize:

A. Do you really need to clutter up the whole bathroom sink with so many lotions, perfumes, sponges, makeup cases, soaps, etc.? Or can they all be put into a cute caddy and placed on a nearby shelf or in a cupboard? Having to dodge a dozen items perched on the sink is a pain in the ass.

B. When I ask what you want to eat, whether it's take-out or going to a restaurant, I really do want to know your preference. I can and will eat anything, so please tell me what you're craving so you'll be happy. Don't get mad at me when I pick a place and afterwards, you're quiet because you didn't want that restaurant.

C. If you're angry with us, tell us as soon as possible. Don't let it simmer inside for days on end. We get nervous when you give us the cold shoulder and we don't know why. Here's the truth: most of us guys are oblivious to whatever bone-headed move we made. If you don't tell us, we can't fix it. Seriously, we're not being stupid on purpose.

D. If I tell you I think you look great, hot, sexy, or any other compliment, please believe me. I mean it. You might be upset because you've gained a few pounds, but I don't care. I think you're gorgeous, so take it to heart when I tell you you're beautiful.

E. I don't like the long, fake nails. They're creepy. Same with the weird eyelashes. And hair extensions. Who/what are you trying to be? I love the real you.

F. Please stop flirting with my friends. Especially in front of me. It's not cute. If you want to flirt and be cute, please do it with ME, especially in front of the guys. I love it when you grab my arm or make it really clear I'm yours. FYI: most of us guys are a little insecure.

G. I'm not ready for kids and putting pressure on me about having them is pushing me the other way more and more. Someday I'll be ready, but not right now.

H. I have no problem when you use my truck, but please, please, please can you put the seat back when you get out? I know this is petty, but when I go to work early in the morning, I'm not looking at my seat when I'm trying to get into my vehicle. It's not until I notice I'm half-wedged into it that I get upset.

I. I know you like shopping for clothes, but you have two whole closets full of clothes with the price tags still on them. I don't get it.

J. More sex. Yeah. I'm saying what we're all thinking. And if you really don't want it that much because I'm not doing it for you, then show me what you like. Tell me what you want. I DO want to please you. Remember, most guys learn from stupid pornos, so . . . yeah. We need you to be a teacher. We're all hot for teacher!

K. If I come home after a 12-hour shift and the lawn is mowed, I swear I'll love you even more than ever.

L. I know my mom is a pain in the ass. But she's still my mom. Can you be nice to her for two hours while we're there?

N. I don't like it when you're on the phone with your friend and you're gossiping. We all talk smack about other people, but when you gossip to one friend about another then turn around and do the same to the first one . . . yeah. Not pretty.

O. I get bitched at about how many guns or fishing poles I have, but never once have I complained about how many shoes and purses she has. Hey, at least my hobbies can put food on the table in case the zombie apocalypse happens.

P. This one is a cliché, but it's oh so true. Please stop taking all my fries. If you wanted some, I'd have gladly paid for another order for you.

WHEW! I confess I'm totally guilty of way too many of the gripes above. Ladies, do you see yourself in any of those items? If so, go ahead and have a heart-to-heart with your guy and see if these comments by my male friends have merit. As for me, I'm always learning. Maybe someday I'll get it right. Or not.

OSCAR STORIES

My father was full of stories from his youth. Those were the days before cell phones, weighted blankets, and safe spaces. Back in the 1940's and 1950's, you could raise a little hell, pull a few shenanigans, and have a good time blowing off steam. My father and his buddies never hurt anyone with their pranks. Oh sure, they may have benefitted now and then, but let's just file those incidents under "creative employment opportunities," shall we?

Oscar King was born in October 1931. He was popular in high school, played sports, was the head of the FFA club and generally well-rounded. As a typical teenage boy, he had plenty of energy for all his activities, even after working on the family farm morning and night. I sometimes laugh at kids today who are SO exhausted after driving their gifted cars to school, then driving home and having to put in a few hours on their computer games before dinner is served. Whew! The stress!

In no particular order, here are a few Oscar stories that I found amusing. One Halloween, Oscar and his buddies decided the local Grange building needed a little bit of decorating. Being a farming community, Malone, New York never lacked for farm equipment sitting in barnyards, fields, or driveways. My father was never too clear on where they acquired the manure spreader, but it happened. In the wee hours of the morning, they procured a full sized, fully functioning, and totally "flavored" shit spreader. These four young lads hauled this piece of equipment into town and somehow managed to hoist it up on the outside top level of the Grange Hall. Now, if any of you are familiar with this piece of equipment, you'll recall the "beaters" are never really clean. The floor of the wagon itself is rarely scraped smooth of its contents. Hauling this monstrosity to the top of the Grange Hall must have been quite a feat. When asked how they did it, a wry smile would cross my father's lips and all he'd say was, "A lot of block and tackle." I remember asking Oscar if he and his buddies were ever caught or disciplined in any way. He just laughed at me and said no. Nobody came after them. Not these bright, young star students and athletes. After being strung up for a few days, my father and his friends generously offered to climb up to the top of the building and get that nasty implement down for the townspeople. What nice young boys. What community-minded young men. People were patting these guys on their backs and thanking them. They even scored a couple of free meals from a local restaurant. Well played, Oscar and crew. Well played.

When you're a farm kid you're usually busy enough doing chores, haying, and doing the constant odd jobs that never seem to end. Once in a blue moon you'll get caught up and have a little bit of free time on your hands. What's that expression? "Idle hands are the Devil's workshop." Okay, so you're a seventeen or eighteen-year-old guy and you need a few bucks for some beer on a Saturday night. What do you do? You don't get paid to work on your own farm. You don't have time to work on someone else's farm. Where do you get the money for a cold beverage or two? Simple. Lover's Lane. Oscar and his pals would toss a couple of shovels, flashlights, and some chains in the back of the old farm truck. They'd head over to the local Lover's Lane area. Which town doesn't have an area like this known to horny young kids? Oscar and crew would go before dark and find the best spots where young Romeos would back their vehicles in and start wooing their Juliets. The one thing these hot Romeos didn't know was that Oscar and his accomplices had taken their shovels and had dug short trenches just about a car's width into the parking spots. The back wheels of the young lovers' vehicles would then get stuck in these trenches. My father and his buddies would just happen to be driving by when they noticed a frustrated youngster trying to rock and roll his car out of that ditch. And gee, Oscar just happened to have tow chains in the back of his truck. Hmmm. For $5 they could pull you out of that ditch and you wouldn't have to call your dad to come get you. What a deal. Making opportunities.

Another thing they liked to do is cruise down Lover's Lane and wait until they saw a car rocking. They'd grab their flashlights, sneak up on the vehicle in motion, snap on the lights, slap the windows, and yell, "IS THAT MY DAUGHTER IN THERE?!" Nothing but arms and legs and clothing flying beyond the steamed windows. The guys would then run back to their truck and head down the road, safe and confident that they may have just prevented an unwanted pregnancy. Oscar and his friends–birth control at its finest.

One of my favorite Oscar stories is the field corn escapade. Occasionally Oscar and the guys would grab their sleeping bags, buy some beer, light a campfire, and just sit around bullshitting like normal kids do. This one evening they decided they'd grab some ears of corn on their way down to the campfire spot. The corn they picked was regular field corn. For those of you who don't know, there's a difference between field corn (for cows) and sweet corn (for humans); however, if you pick the field corn early enough, it's still sweet and juicy and delicious. You also must remember, this was back in the late 1940's and early 1950's. People weren't so spoiled and high maintenance back then. Having been through a war or two, people just weren't that picky about food. Armed with a couple of burlap feedbags, Oscar and his goons picked a few dozen ears of corn and proceeded to the campfire spot. Beers were had. Many beers were had. Then the gents started getting hungry, so they carefully placed the unhusked ears of field corn in the coals of the fire. They turned the ears a few times, so they'd be evenly cooked. The hungry guys dug into that delicious corn. They ate and ate until they were stuffed. More beers were consumed, more jokes and stories told, until finally, in the wee hours of the morning, they called it quits and bedded down for the night. Snuggled in sleeping bags and blankets, bellies full of beer and corn, they all fell asleep happy and content. The next morning, they were moving a little slowly. One by one they woke up, scratched, farted, and burped. One of the guys, Johnny, announced he was starving. Nothing like hangover hunger. He reached into the now cooled coals of the previous night's fire and pulled an ear of corn out of it. He shucked it and gagged. It was full of corn borers. He grabbed another ear. Same thing. By this time the other guys were gathering around, each grabbing an ear of corn only to find that each ear of corn was LOADED with corn borers. In case you're not familiar with what corn borers (or as they call them up here, corn bores) are, they're little worms about an inch long, and cream colored. They love any kind of grain. Oh, how I would have loved to have been a fly on a shoulder that morning, watching all those young men turning green. Bad enough they were feeling the effects of the brown bottle flu. Add in the fact that they all had bellies full of . . . um . . . yeah. To this day, I can't see sweet corn at a roadside stand or in the grocery store without thinking of my father and his friends.

Oscar had numerous stories and I loved hearing them repeatedly. I only wish I'd written down more of his tales. The best stories are always the true ones, and he had them by the dozens.

MIND SHADOWS

The days all pass the same.
Quietly.
I'm imprisoned in my body.
My thoughts leaking drop by drop.

My life now reduced to darkness and grays.
I have mind shadows.
These eyes don't focus anymore.
They open but they don't see.

I can still feel my heart beating.
I know I'm alive.
But does anyone else know?
The slow thumping goes on and on.

Words can't form on my lips.
My hands won't even reach for you.
Please reach for me.
Don't forget I'm still here.

** Dedicated to Oscar and everyone else
dealing with Alzheimer's. **

AN UNDERSTANDING

Here he comes again, I thought to myself. That old guy who loves to talk. I'd just finished weeding a few rows in our huge garden when old Teddy pedaled his bicycle into the driveway. He was a harmless old man, but he was out there, if you know what I mean. I was just a kid, only about 13 years old or so, but old enough to know when someone's elevator isn't hitting all the floors. The locals knew Teddy to be a storyteller, but they agreed some of his tales had a smidgeon of truth to them.It was sometimes difficult to figure out if he was pulling your leg, or if he was telling the truth. Still, he was fun to listen to and what did it hurt to let him spin a yarn or two?

Teddy used to tell stories of his years on the railroad. The hard work he did, the towns he'd seen, the booze and wild women of which he'd had his fair share. He retired from the railroad and lived off a small pension. His home was a modest cabin on his grandson's property near the state forest not far from our farm.

Old Teddy pulled in and dismounted from his bike. "Hey honey, could I please trouble you for some water?" I nodded and he headed for the hose attached to the side of our house. He'd stopped in several times before and never wanted to be a burden and always asked politely for water. Teddy cranked on the spigot and waited a minute for the warm water in the hose to come out. When the water turned cool, he puckered his old lips and drank several long gulps. He whipped out an old faded red bandana and wet it. Wiping his brow and neck with it, he smiled at me and winked. He took a few more sips of water then turned the hose off and hung it back on the hook.

"Mind if I set a spell? This heat has me feeling a little lazy today." My father was in the barn and my mother was in the kitchen, so I didn't see any problem with Old Teddy taking a break. I was sitting on the bench underneath the window in full view of my mother as she busied herself in the kitchen. She looked out at one point and said hi to Teddy. He waved back and thanked her for the water. Teddy sat down on the other end of the bench and let out a big sigh. "Whew! You just don't know you're getting older until you're there!" Then he chuckled a bit. We chatted about the garden and how much hay we'd put in so far that summer. After a while he launched into one of his stories.

"I used to hunt all the land around here when I was just a kid. I know these fields and woods inside and out. The farmers used to let a few of us fellas take a deer or two in the fall as long as we got one for them too. We had to shoot a bunch of the racoons eating all the field corn as part of the deal. Pretty good bargain, don'tcha think?" Teddy nodded as if he was agreeing with himself. "All of us guys had an understanding with the farmers and with each other. Nobody got selfish or greedy. We'd all talk about who was going to this farm or that one and we never stepped on each other's toes. It was a great system that worked out for all of us. That is, except for Jerry. Let me tell you about Jerry." And with that comment, Teddy leaned forward and spat on the dirt driveway. I don't know if he had something in his mouth, or if just the thought of this Jerry guy left a bitter taste with him.

"Jerry was out for himself. Always had been. He'd take your last dime if you left it alone for a second." Teddy's wrinkled face looked pinched as his eyes narrowed and his jaw set. "It wasn't as if he needed more than anyone else. Hell, truth be told, he had more than most of us. Years ago, his family had a hotel up in Lake Placid, and they did pretty good in the tourist business. When they died, he inherited a pile of cash. I think it was just a game to Jerry, to get more than the rest of us, selfish bastard that he was." I noticed Teddy's hands were gripping the seat of the bench. He relaxed after a minute or so and continued with his story. "He didn't have a wife or kids to feed. He wasn't hungry. He was just greedy."

I shifted on the bench and watched him closely.

"One day I was hunting right back here a might, and who do I see but Jerry!" Teddy shook his head, his jowls wobbling from one side to the other. "I told him this here's my territory and he can't be on it. I told him the farmer, Al, said I was the only one allowed back there. Well, that didn't mean anything to him at all! He just laughed at me and said he'd hunt wherever he damned well pleased! I left the back field and went straight to the barn. I talked to Al, and he said he only gave me permission to hunt here, nobody else. When I told him Jerry's in his back lot, he wasn't happy. Al said he'd have a word with him and straighten this all out."

"And did Jerry leave after that? Did you end up being the only one hunting here?" I asked.

"Nope! That son of a bitch kept coming back. Whenever I saw him, he'd just laugh and walk away from me. He'd let off a few rounds just to scare away any deer that might be around so I wouldn't have a chance of getting one. I didn't want to be like a whiny kid and go running to the farmer, but what else could I do? I was supposed to hold up my end of the bargain and get a deer for him and at least one for myself. I'm a man of my word and I intended to keep it." I noticed Teddy sat up a little straighter and his chin lifted half an inch or so. Being a man of his word was important, as it should be to all of us.

"What did you do? Did you call the police or the environmental conservation department or anyone?" I was getting angry on his behalf, even though this had taken place many years before my time.

"Honey, back then you didn't call the police. You didn't call anyone. You handled it yourself. I talked to Al, and he said he'd have another word with Jerry. And he did. He said they came to an understanding. I was relieved that the mess was sorted out between them. It was the end of hunting season anyway, so I wound up bagging a couple of deer off state land. One for me, and one for Al because I knew Jerry had spooked all the deer on Al's property."

I was glad to hear he could keep his word to the farmer, Al. Even as a young man, Teddy knew the value of giving one's word.

"We had a mild winter that year. Then spring came. I was working a lot. Summer came and was hot and buggy. Then finally it was hunting season again. I got together with my buddies, and we divvied up the farms like usual. I got Al's farm again because I knew it better than anyone else. And I'll admit, I wanted to see if Jerry had the balls to come back again." I could see the determination in Teddy's eyes. He wasn't going to take any crap from Jerry that hunting season.

"I bagged a rugged buck on my third trip out to the back meadow, right next to a big maple tree. Al told me to take that one home, and he'd keep the next one . . . if I got another one, that is." Teddy held his hands up pointing towards the sky and said, "As if I couldn't?" and he laughed. "I hadn't run into Jerry yet, so I was pretty happy about that. Maybe he went to someone else's farm to poach that year. That's what I was hoping, anyway. Must be the talk Al had with him had stuck."

I loved watching Teddy's face light up as he talked about his stress-free hunting season. He remembered how happy he was knowing Jerry wouldn't be bothering him again.

"Three days later I went back to the very same spot and wouldn't you know it, there was another buck, a huge one, just waiting for me to drop him. Almost as if he was daring me to take him. So, I did. I gutted him not too far from where I dressed out the first one and dragged it back to the barn. I went to hang it up in the heifer barn as usual, but Al caught me before I got there and asked me to hang it in on the hook just outside the machinery shed instead. It was an impressive-looking deer, so I figured he wanted people to see it as they drove by his place. I hung it up where he wanted it, said good night, and went home."

"So, no sign of Jerry while you were hunting?" I queried.

"Nope. I guess he gave up on Al's property. I was relieved. A week or so later, I decided to see if I could snag a doe on Al's property. He had that one buck, but a second deer for the freezer would be welcomed by his family, that's for sure. I walked to that back meadow again but this time I went right to the place where I'd dropped the bucks. I walked around the big old maple tree that was in the corner, and I saw something that I hadn't noticed before. I saw a sizable patch of clover and alfalfa. I didn't remember that being there the previous year, but then again, I didn't go behind that tree, just near it. I stuck mainly to the trails and the open meadow. I looked around and there wasn't any alfalfa or clover anywhere else. It was just this one big patch, and not even where you could get to it for haying. As I was walking through it, I noticed the ground was kind of bumpy and uneven, so I figured the deer must have been pawing and digging at it when they were eating. That's how they got so fat. Anyway, I went back to my usual spot and waited. After a couple of hours, a nice doe showed up behind the maple tree. I waited until she came around the front and popped her with one shot. Down she went. That made two for Al's freezer." Teddy held up a hand with two fingers extended for punctuation.

"Sounds to me like everything went your way that year. Glad things worked out just fine." I gave Teddy a grin and two thumbs up.

"Yup, it did. I dragged the doe back to Al's barn. He was out cutting corn, so I went to the heifer barn to hang the doe. I opened the doors, found a rope, and strung her up. I went to tie her off to the hook near the back of the door frame, and that's when I saw something." Teddy's eyebrows went up a notch. "I saw a burlap bag that was empty. And next to it was a round-pointed shovel. Not a square-tipped shovel you use for moving manure. Nope. A digging shovel." His eyes got a little bigger.

"Okay, an empty bag. A shovel. Typical farm stuff, right?" I wasn't catching what he was pitching.

"The bag was a clover-alfalfa seed mix," Teddy explained.

"Yeah, okay. So, he baited the deer for you? Made a food plot? That was legal back then, right? I mean, after all, it was on his own land. Maybe he was making up for you getting skunked the year before?" I asked.

"I thought so too, at first. But later that week when I saw Al, I casually asked him if he'd seen Jerry at all this hunting season. You know what he told me?"

"I have no idea."

"His exact words were, 'Teddy, last I knew, Jerry was out feeding the deer' and then the very corner of his lips turned up just a tiny bit. And he went back to his chores."

I let this sink in for a minute. Teddy watched me. My expression must have changed from confusion to conclusion at what he just implied. I didn't say a word. Teddy was silent.

Teddy then stood up and said, "Well, I'd better get going. I still have a few miles to go before I get home." Then he picked up his bike and threw one leg over the bar and sat down on the seat. He was just about to pedal off down the driveway when he paused and looked over his shoulder at me.

"Nobody ever saw Jerry after that first hunting season I told you about. We all just figured he must have moved away." And with a wink, Teddy turned his bike toward the road and started pedaling.

The big maple tree still stands in the corner of the back

meadow. There isn't any alfalfa or clover growing behind it now, just scrub brush. There's a big rock that sits near the tree too. Still, sometimes when I walk back there, I remember Teddy's story and look behind that old tree.

AB POSITIVE

"C'mon, PJ. You'll feel wonderful afterwards. It's truly the gift of life."

I shook my head at my friend and co-worker, Connie's, words. How on earth would I donate blood? I passed out in Mrs. Nandal's biology class when she was just talking about pricking our fingers and finding out our blood type.

I'm the one who has dropped not once, but twice in the emergency room when I took my mother in for pneumonia as they hooked her up to IVs. I'm a wimp when it comes to needles and blood. I've never made that a secret. As a matter of fact, every year when the ACME Medical trailer came to my job for our annual physicals, the guys I worked with used to take bets on whether I'd drop and do the chicken when the nurse took my blood. The scheduler used to make sure one of the bigger guys was slotted in at the same time with me just in case I needed to be picked up off the floor. No lie.

"But Connie, I'll pass out. I'll throw up and THEN pass out." My solid reasons for not donating blood at the company blood drive fell on deaf ears.

"You can do it, PJ. You can take your time getting up. They have juice and cookies when you're done. Seriously, you'll be saving lives." Damn you, Connie. Who doesn't want to be a hero? Or in my case, heroine? I finally said yes and told Connie I'd meet her up on the third floor at 9:00 the following Tuesday.

Tuesday came way too quickly. I had read the pamphlets. I had eaten a good breakfast a couple of hours earlier. I had plenty of water the night before and that morning. I wore comfortable clothing. I was going to SAVE LIVES!

I stepped off the elevator and walked into the display room that was closed off to the public that day. There stood four nurses all smiling like vampires in scrubs. Another lady was at a table near the doorway. "Name?"

I gave her my name and told her it was my first time, and to please be gentle. She laughed and said it would be easy. Thousands of people donate blood every single day. Piece of cake.

People lie.

After a few minutes of paperwork, I was shown to a table. It was quite comfy. Padded, clean sheets. A crisp pillowcase. The nurse gave me a soft, happy look and thanked me for coming in and for giving the gift of life. I looked over at the next table and there was Connie, already tapped like a maple tree, giving me the thumbs-up.

I warned the nurse that I was a tad bit squeamish and prone to passing out around needles and blood. "Don't worry. We'll keep a good eye on you." She then swabbed me from what felt like my armpit to my wrist with cold rubbing alcohol. The smell of it alone started me down Queasy Street. I closed my eyes and started thinking of Tom Selleck as Magnum, P.I. I thought if my normally low blood pressure went any lower, I really should bump it up a little bit. Couldn't hurt to try. The nurse then stuck a six-inch needle into my arm right at the crook of my elbow and I'm pretty sure it hit my shoulder socket. I wanted to back out, but I figured okay, this was the worst of it. I could do this. Thomas Magnum . . . walking out of the blue Hawaiian water with those short swim trunks on . . . Magnum in his red Ferrari . . . Thomas wiggling his eyebrows. I've got this.

I took deep breaths. I thought of baking cookies. I thought of kickboxing class. I thought of saving lives and how noble I'd be if I could get to the end of this nightmare. Finally, after what seemed like an hour (which it wasn't, I'm sure), the nurse took the needle out of my body, stuck a cotton ball on the gaping hole, and taped it securely to my skin.

I DID IT! I was screaming that in my head. I DONATED BLOOD! Connie came over to my table and said, "See? I knew you could do it. Don't you feel wonderful?"

I looked up at her through my glossy eyes, a little hazy and sweaty, and smiled. "Yeah, I'm pretty impressed I didn't pass out."

I started to sit up because I could see the cookies and juice about ten feet from me. My blood ain't free, woman. No sir. It's going to cost you some sweets. About ten seconds after I sat up, I broke out into a cold sweat. The room started spinning like a Las

Vegas roulette wheel. The nurse looked at me and calmly advised me to lie back down. I did as I was told because, really, what choice did I have? I couldn't have jumped off the table and taken a few steps if I'd wanted. She grabbed a few pillows and propped my legs up. Then she placed cold, wet towels on my forehead and on the back of my neck.

Connie brought over a cup of juice with a straw and gave me a few sips. "You just need to get your sugar back up. Nothing to worry about," she reassured me.

After half a glass of orange juice and a crunchy cookie, I felt ready to try again. I eased my way up and this time swung my legs over the table. Yes! That one minor blip wasn't going to stop me. I was good to go.

Or not.

The room started spinning again. This time it was a free ride on the tilt-a-whirl. Everyone sounded like they were in a silo. Back down I went. My total table time was almost two hours from start to finish. Surely, they must have taken five gallons of my precious blood. Why else would I feel like such a disaster?

I eventually regained my bearings and was able to walk on my own. The lady at the front table with all the paperwork stopped me on my way out and asked me if I was on any lists? What lists? I'm sure I'm on a lot of peoples' lists, but which one did she mean? "Young lady, you're an AB positive. That's a rare blood type. We like to keep people on lists in case of emergencies. We'd like to keep you in mind in the event we need your particular blood type." Oh. That list.

My head still wasn't quite right, but I remember just nodding at her. I was letting her know I understood what she was saying. She took it to mean I wanted to be on her special list. Thankfully, the American Red Cross never called me for any AB positive emergency, but that's because of my next episode.

Fast forward a year or so later. I picked up my mother and we went to Malone to do some shopping. On our way home, we passed by the fire station and there was a big wooden sign out front: BLOOD DONORS NEEDED! The firemen were having a blood drive. By this time, the memory of getting queasy and sweaty at the blood drive at my job had faded somewhat. What really stuck in my mind was that fantastic feeling of knowing I helped someone at their darkest hour. When they really needed life's juice, I had delivered. I looked over at my mother and asked her if she wanted to donate blood. "I've never given blood except for the usual hospital tests. Yeah, let's do it!" Apparently, the Hero complex is real. And I had it.

We confidently walked into the fire station and were immediately met by several fire fighters. They had the Malone Firemen t-shirts on, smiling ear to ear, and were thanking us for stopping in. Already we felt like queens. The first thing out of my mouth was, "I'm an AB POSITIVE as if that would guarantee me special treatment. Maybe they'd even name a holiday after me. We did the obligatory paperwork and moved on to our respective tables. I cautioned the gentleman doing my vein drain that I was very much a coward and maybe, just maybe, I might get a little queasy. He said not to worry. He'd done this thousands of times and could handle anything. Excellent!

The blood drive was getting busy. There were several more tables and cots and people were laughing, chatting, and generally having a good time. I glanced over at my mother, and she was having an animated conversation and fun time with her own personal Dracula. Nothing like bonding over bloodletting.

My guy swabbed my arm and put the needle in. I knew what to expect this time, so I wasn't as hyped up about it. He was chatting with me and then suddenly it was like a cold tidal wave washed over me. I started to sweat. But I was cold. I became super dizzy. I told my medical Shop-Vac dude. He just said, "Aww, it'll pass, just hang in there. Now tell me again, where do you work and what do you do?"

My mind was working hard to concentrate. I started telling him I worked at the Power Authority, but it came out "Pawww Torty." I sounded like a stroke victim. I tried again. "PAWWWW TORTY!" That was when my eyesight started fading. I was blinking but I couldn't see anything. I could have sworn I was riding the Sphinx and waving to dead relatives. I started to panic. "I CANNNN'T SEE!" I was shaking my head back and forth and fluttering my eyelids, but I only saw black.

I heard the lady supervisor who had been walking around the room come over and say to my nurse, "We're losing her! Take it out!" My nurse began stalling. I could HEAR everything. I couldn't SEE anything, but I could hear.

"Oh . . . (long pause) she's almost done . . . (pause) though." I couldn't visually confirm, but I'm pretty sure he was rolling my feet up like a tube of toothpaste, trying to squeeze more blood out of me.

"I CANNNN'T SEEEEEE!" I sounded like Jodi Foster's character in *Nell*. I began crying then.

"TAKE IT OUT! TAKE IT OUT NOW!" The supervisor must have been watching me blink, sweat, slur.

I could hear my tormentor ask, "You mean . . . right . . . now? I mean, she only needs a few more minutes to . . . ."

"I SAID TAKE IT OUT NOW! WE'RE LOSING HER! SHE'S GOING INTO SHOCK!" Bless her heart. Angels do walk among us.

At that moment I felt my arm being jostled about and then tape being put on in the crook of my elbow.

I heard some minor mumbling from my nurse. Obviously, I pissed him off by going into shock and not letting him get the full five-gallon bucket of my precious red liquid.

Remember, my mother was only a few tables away. She'd already donated her bag-o-blood and was enjoying a cup of juice and a cookie. She was watching me and waiting patiently. Then she noticed things weren't going quite as well as she was expecting. Four people were gathered around me. Legs propped up, ice pack on my head, blood pressure cuff on my other arm. This is not what any mother wants to see happening to her child, no matter what that child's age.

The nurses and the supervisor managed to get me off the table and into a wheelchair. They pushed me around a truck and a screen and kept me out of sight. I guess I was bad for business. The supervisor came to me with refreshments. She told me the guy who oversaw taking my blood had been reassigned to the paperwork desk because I was the second person today that he was a bit slow in terminating the donation.

She did, however, assure me that I donated enough blood that it could be broken down and the plasma could be used in a hospital setting, or that the partial pint I donated would be enough for a child. She was really trying to give me an out. She was so concerned that I felt worthless. I never did get her name, but I remembered her kindness and compassion.

It took another half hour or so before I rejoined the living. At this point, the supervisor came over to me with my Red Cross blood donor card and showed me where she had marked it. She told me how much the Red Cross appreciated my efforts, but even though I'm an AB positive, I'm just more trouble than I'm worth. She said it in the nicest way possible, but the fact remains that I was rejected by the American Red Cross. Says so on my card.

My mother decided she'd drive us home from Malone. Which is a good thing because as I was sitting there in the passenger seat of my car, I looked down and apparently, I had sprung a leak. My right arm was leaking red fluid all over my bright yellow sweatshirt sleeve. I grabbed some napkins out of the glovebox and pressed them to my arm as I held it up over my head. My mother, ever so sweet, just laughed and said, "That lady was right. You ARE more trouble than your blood is worth." We made it back to my parents' house and I crashed on their couch for a little while. My mother rebandaged my arm and all was fine in my world.

That was the last time I attempted to give blood. Can you blame me?

RANDOM THOUGHTS

1. Hummingbird vs. Cattle

Fast. Faster. As I watch the ambitious hummingbirds at my red plastic feeders hanging from my tree, I can almost hear their thoughts. "This spot is good." "That one looks better." "I should move over there." Never content with what's right in front of them, even though it's all the same feeder, all the same sugar water. Darting this way, that way, searching for more sweetness with every jabbing of their long beaks. Reminds me of human nature.

We flit around in our lives, looking for that elusive "better" prize. I'm not talking about bettering your education, your job, your home, or personal life. Better IS good. I'm talking about when you already have a great life, and you still aren't happy. What next? Why do we stress and struggle chasing what we think will make us happier, and in the end it doesn't? When is enough enough? My mother used to say if you have your health, you have everything. I think she was right about that. Still, we're just human beings and it's natural to want more. More money and possessions. More friends. More experiences. Sometimes it seems we're just hamsters on the wheel, running so fast and so hard that we're wearing ourselves out in pursuit of a happiness we'll never catch.

I look past the hummingbird feeder and see the wide-open meadow dotted with grazing beef cattle. I notice they're not in a hurry. Not flitting about from one area to another. These beasts are taking their time, eating slowly, and occasionally they'll raise their heads to look around then resume mowing the grass beneath them. I see how calm and relaxed they are, and I think to myself, that's the way we need to be. We need to take lessons from cattle. Although it's always been an insult to be called a cow, I think I'll make an exception now. I want to be a cow.

2. Sunrise Thoughts

My coffee genie swirls and rises from my cup as I settle into the tall deck chair. The sun is hinting at its visit. Any moment now it'll stretch up and claim a spot in the sky, pushing out the darkness of last night.

Countless possibilities await in this brand new, never seen before glow. A gift. Another day to be alive. To be happy. To forgive myself for not being perfect yesterday. Or the day before.

Tree branches subtly wave good morning to me. They know I'll make plans for the day, but they also remind me to be flexible, to sway as needed. As my eyes wander across the green grassy carpet of my front lawn, I notice the living, moving, vibrant trees filled with plump emerald leaves providing shade and shelter. My eyes are then drawn to the stark, cold telephone pole. It was once a tree that supplied life Now it's only utilitarian, stripped of its beauty and just doing its job. No swaying, no dancing, no whispers when a breeze graces the barren structure. It is empty of any happiness it may have had in a previous life.

Is this what we've become? We start out happy and full of life. We laugh, play, love, and live. We dance to the music in our hearts and minds. Then real life hits us, and we must work, pay bills, and accept adult responsibilities. Where is it written we must sacrifice all of our branches and leaves? There must be a happy medium somewhere in this life.

Starting today, I'm going to regrow my leaves. I'm going to flutter in the wind and feel the gentle caress of nature's breath on my limbs. I'm going to provide shelter and sustenance to those who need it. Time will eventually make me a telephone pole, but until that moment comes, I plan to lift my face to the sun, sink my roots deep into the earth, and love every minute of real life and the absolute joy it brings.

3. Stones

We've all heard the songs about stones, mainly our gravestones and how it's that dash in between the dates chiseled that's important. I couldn't agree more. We move from birthstones to tombstones. Some people get bullied and have stones thrown at them. Other people get stoned on substances that take them away from reality for a while. We've given each other stone-cold looks. In the city, if you're looking for a good restaurant, you're only a stone's throw from one. When we're not under the influence, we say we're stone cold sober. Standing at a pond it's fun to be skipping stones. If you're living in a glass house, it may behoove you to never throw stones. I've known people with stone-cold hearts. They'll never love at all. That's written in stone. We build stone walls around our properties to mark our territory and to keep intruders out. We build stone walls around our hearts to keep from getting hurt again, but that's never really set in stone, is it? Then there are people like rolling stones as they gather no moss (and I don't mean Mick Jagger). When we improve our lives, we use steppingstones to reach our goals. When someone is lazy and won't work to pay back the money they owe you, you're out of luck because you can't get blood from a stone. I don't condone violence, but if you can kill two birds with one stone, you're doing well. Someday I might kiss the Blarney Stone for good luck. And don't forget, let he who is without sin cast the first stone.

BIG SACK O' FLOUR

You're familiar with my mother's pepperoni story and how silly we could get in the grocery store, right? How about another grocery store tale?

One afternoon we were in that same store doing the usual boring grocery shopping. The only difference that day was Ma had hurt her foot the day before and wanted to push the cart so she could lean on it. She didn't break her foot or anything but twisted it and just needed a little help. Back then they didn't have those electric carts for people to ride around on in the store. We switched positions for that trip.

I walked ahead of the cart, and she'd point out which products to select, how many, what brand, etc. I picked out exactly what she wanted as she slowly inched the cart forward, leaning on the handle to take the weight off her bad foot.

We came up to the baking section and she asked me to get one of those forty-pound bags of flour. Now remember, when you're cooking for a family of eight, you always buy the BIG bags, cans, jars, etc. I looked at the shelves and down on the bottom shelf the big bags of flour were stacked. I bent my knees, wrapped my hands around it, and balanced it with my forearms as I pulled it off the shelf. As I began to straighten my knees to stand, Ma cautioned urgently, in a very loud voice, "PENDRA! BE CAREFUL OF YOUR UTERUS!"

My knees buckled and the bag of flour dropped about four inches to the floor. Didn't break open or anything, thankfully. I started laughing and turned to look at her and her face was straight . . . for the most part. I could see her eyes twinkling and the corners of her mouth were twitching. That's when I noticed about three other women standing within earshot staring at me. I got myself together, picked up the big bag of flour and gently placed it in the cart. The women walked around us. I didn't dare look at any of them directly, but I could tell they were giving me such odd looks.

That's when I started giggling again and between sputters and spurts asked Ma, "What the Hell does my UTERUS have to do with flour?"

She grinned slightly at me and then with great effort, kept her face straight and said, "Back in the olden days a woman wasn't supposed to lift anything heavy because it could hurt her uterus and cause it to fall out!" Then her lips parted, and she roared.

Guess what I think about when I pass the big bags of flour? And yes, maybe I do an extra Kegel squeeze or two just to make sure nothing's falling out.

ROCKY

A few years ago, my sweet friend Marcy gave me a wall hanging of my favorite actor's character and his famous speech in one of his movies. I have it hanging on my bedroom wall. I give it a nod every morning as my eyes open, and another nod before I climb into bed at night. I'm sure most of you are familiar with Sylvester Stallone's "The world ain't all sunshine and rainbows" monologue. Say what you will about Rocky Balboa, but I believe if you took the time to really watch and LISTEN to what happens in that movie series, you'll learn a lot more about life than you imagined possible.

It's May 1st today. Early this morning I slithered out of my elevated queen-sized bed, gave Rocky a nod, then headed to the kitchen to turn on my life support system (the coffee pot). By 6:00 a.m. I hit the shower to sing along to Gary Allan's best cd to date: *Ruthless*. I donned an old Colton 10-Miler race t-shirt and my hoga pants. My WHAT, you ask? That's what I dubbed these yoga pants that have two built-in holsters to carry my Glock. Holster + yoga = hoga. Get it? Don't worry, you'll get used to how my mind works.

Fresh and ready to start my day, I poured my first cup of nectar of the gods and headed for my front deck. It's an early Sunday morning and that big ball of fire in the sky is kissing the dewy grass. I hiked my ample bottom up onto the tall deck chair and perched there enjoying my hot caffeinated beverage and the silence of my little corner of the world. I do my best thinking when it's quiet with only the sounds of nature to remind me I'm not in a vacuum. As I sat there, I pondered the latest book I'd read about positive thinking. It had some great points but also a lot of hokey stuff between the covers. Still, I'm one of those people who can take what applies to my life and leave the rest. One of the points in that book was whenever you're having a negative thought, replace it with at least two positive ones. It's not always easy, but it does get better with practice.

This morning I'm not having any negative thoughts at all. That made me realize how lucky I am and how someone somewhere has blessed me with a good attitude. At least for today. I thought of the Rocky hanging Marcy had given me. I thought about the multitude of sunshine and rainbows in my life and started counting a few. I looked to my right and saw the first tulip of the season had bloomed. Its bright yellow petals defiantly screamed, "THE DEER DIDN'T GET ME THIS SPRING!" I laughed. I looked to my left and saw a handful of sleepy tulips getting ready to open and share their beauty any moment now. Closer to the sidewalk is a tiny purple flower sprouting up through the decorative landscaping stones. I call those blooms "accidentals" because four years ago I had planted these flowers in the garden pots, but they spread by themselves, quite accidentally. They've taken over the area between my sidewalk and house, and I'm delighted every spring when they push their way through the little stones and grace me with their presence.

As I sipped and counted, my list became longer. I could feel the warmth of the sun on my skin. My ears picked up the melodious songs of various birds. My eyes tracked the graceful ducks flying overhead on their way to the winding stream just down the road. Now and then a vehicle would drive by, and I'd raise my hand to wave, or lift my coffee cup as if to say, "Good morning to you!" I love the smiles and waves returned by these early morning travelers.

That's when it hit me. I need to make a list. I'm a chronic list maker and will not apologize for it. Lists keep me on track and let me know I'm not as lazy as I tell myself. Lists give me a feeling of accomplishment, even on the days when my lists are something like this: (1) get up and shower, (2) drink coffee, (3) watch Netflix. Even on THOSE days when I can check such daunting tasks off my list, I feel productive. I've decided for the month of May I'll keep a running list of all the sunshine and rainbows that bring me joy. I'm sure there will be mostly minute moments of happiness that, if I'm not looking for them, may pass me by without my even noticing. I'm going to be more aware of these "S&R" moments or items that make me smile and add them to my list. With any luck at all, I'll use a lot of paper.

These "S&R" moments will hopefully combat the negative

or sad moments that creep into everyday life. For instance, Mother's Day is coming up next week. My mother said adios in October 2002, so Mother's Day isn't all that happy anymore. Some of you will get me. And if you don't, I'm happy for you. Give your mom a few extra hugs when you can. Thanks. I'm sure something in my house will break, leak, or just decide to not work one day. I'll try to take that inconvenience with a grain of salt. If I get too snarky or down, I'll consult my "S&R" list as a reminder of just how good I have it.

I realize I've touched on this topic of creating your own happiness before, but really, can you ever be TOO positive? I totally get we can't be blind to the sorrow and sadness in the world. It's all around us; however, we can be like Rocky Balboa. We can take the hits and keep getting back up. We can stand up for the ones we love and fight the good fight. We can look around us and see who has stuck by us during our most difficult times, and who was there only when we were on top. The truth comes out eventually, and it's always better late than never. Find the people, places, and experiences that make you truly happy and don't let anyone or anything stop you.

Find your Rocky. Look for your sunshine and rainbows. They're there. Right in front of you. You may not win the multi-million-dollar lottery this week. Or next. But do you have someone to hug? Do you have enough food? Can you get outside and listen to nature? Start replacing those negatives with double positives. I swear on a stack of chocolate (which you KNOW is sacred to me) that this swapping works.

So, in case I haven't thanked you enough, THANK YOU Marcy Smutz! I'll keep Rocky's words of wisdom and his never-say-die attitude for as long as humanly possible.

I'm pretty sure I'm going to need more paper for my Sunshine and Rainbows list this month.

42ND BIRTHDAY

Birthdays. Who doesn't love birthdays? Ever since I was a little kid, I knew birthdays were special. My mother would bake a cake and put the hard store-bought candies that spelled "HAPPY BIRTHDAY" on it with the required number of candles. Happy Birthday was sung by the folks and other siblings and the birthday child would then get to blow out the candles and make a wish. Sometimes the candles would get relit and younger siblings could spray the cake with their wishes too. Ahhh, life in a big family. But that's when I developed my love of birthdays. We didn't have much, but my mother made sure every birthday was a big deal. Many years later when one of my older brothers was killed by a drunk driver at the tender age of 26, I started appreciating birthdays even more. I was never one to whine about turning thirty or forty or more. I figured each birthday I was allowed was a gift and one not to be taken lightly.

Anyone who knows me understands I'm not a high maintenance woman. I don't like the spotlight. I don't like constant gifts, attention, and fawning all over me. That's just not me. HOWEVER, three days a year I do want to feel special: (1) my birthday, (2) Valentine's Day, (3) Christmas. One needn't go overboard. Just get me a sweet card, write something mushy in it, and give me a small gift that fits my lifestyle, interests, hobbies or whatever you think is "me."

And this brings me to the story of my 42nd birthday. Around September of that year, I started dating a guy I'll call Jack. Jack was a lot like me. About my age, never been married, no kids, owned his own home, financially secure, good job, loved his family, and so on. He was intelligent and very up on current events. At six feet tall, slender build, sandy blonde hair and amazingly bright blue eyes, I figured we were somewhat matched on the attraction scale. I'm five-foot-four, brown hair, and average weight. Not a supermodel, yet not a wildebeest. Sometimes he could be a little annoying when he found something to bitch about but, hey, can't we all? I gave him a heads-up in October that my birthday was coming up in November and as he knew by then, I didn't ask for much. He came straight out and asked what I wanted for my birthday. I loved his direct, no-nonsense attitude. So, I let him have it, much like little Ralphie Parker telling Santa about the Red Ryder bb gun for Christmas. "I'd like a sentimental birthday card. I'd like to go to a sit-down restaurant with tablecloths. I'd love a nice dinner and a piece of cake for dessert. Then I'd like you to spend the night with me at my house." He laughed and said that wasn't too hard to do. I was delighted.

Shortly after that conversation I had to go out of town for my job for a few days. One of those evenings away I stopped by a bustling mall and found a sleek little black dress that would be perfect for an evening dinner. When I got home Jack came over for dinner one evening and I pulled the dress out to show him. I excitedly told him, "This is the dress I'm wearing on my birthday when we go out to dinner." He smiled and said it was gorgeous. He knew I didn't dress up often and it took a lot of effort on my part to "girly it up" for a special occasion.

The days came and went. Then finally it was my birthday. I had spent the previous night at Jack's house because for some reason he never wanted to stay at my home. In hindsight, I'm guessing it had to do with my lack of beverage choices and cable TV. It was the morning of my birthday. He had to go to work early and was gone by the time I got out of bed. I walked to his kitchen and propped up on the table was a card. I eagerly ripped open the envelope and out slid two packets of hand warmers. You know, the kind in the little plastic pouches that you open, and they activate once the air hits them. You put them in your gloves or mittens on chilly days. I figured aha! This is a hint! He's going to get me a nice pair of gloves to keep my hands warm. Or maybe we're going somewhere that I'll need the extra warmth. An outdoor show of some sort? Hmmm? I read the card. It was a simple, generic card that you could give to your boss, grandmother, or mailman. Nothing mushy written inside, just signed "Jack." No biggie I thought to myself as I got ready to head home and start my day. To be honest, we'd only been dating for two months and maybe he didn't feel that mushy toward me yet. I understand.

Around 5:00 p.m. I started getting ready for dinner. I showered, shaved, lotioned, plucked, buffed, and polished. Seriously, it takes this woman a lot of effort to look girly. At about 6:00 p.m. Jack walked in, and his eyes popped out of his head.

"WOW! You look HOT!" I smiled and said thank you. Who doesn't like their hard work noticed? That's when I noticed what he was wearing: a long-sleeved t-shirt with a skateboarder logo on it, old worn-out jeans, beat up sneakers. Hmmm. Jack said, "Gee, I guess I should have dressed up a little bit. Compared to you, I look like shit." I distinctly remembered showing him that dress and telling him I'd be wearing it, so it's not like he didn't have a clue as to how gussied up I'd be on that evening. I just shrugged and told him it didn't matter as long as he was comfortable. Then I asked where we were going for dinner. At that point I noticed a subtle change in his demeanor. Almost angry. He said he didn't know.

HUH? I casually asked, "Did you make reservations anywhere?" He looked at me like I had a turtle on my head.

He replied, "Uhhh, no. Was I supposed to?" By now I'm thinking it's the North Country so maybe things aren't that busy tonight.

I said, "Well, it's a Tuesday, so it might not be necessary."

That's when he said in a frustrated tone, "Okay, you pick a place and call for a reservation, and we'll go." Confused, I picked up my phone and called a local place that wasn't too expensive yet not a drive thru. They said yes, they could reserve a table for two for seven o'clock. Excellent!

I grabbed my little clutch purse that matched my dress and we headed for the door. Jack was already out the door and on the sidewalk before I could shrug into my coat. He must have been extremely hungry, right? I was wearing heels this evening. Not super high cfm's, but maybe two-inch heels. And did I mention I have a hard time with this stuff? I was ever so slowly teetering out my door, onto the freshly snow-covered sidewalk, and trying to make it to the driveway without twisting an ankle or flying flat on my face. I looked up and there was Jack already sitting in his vehicle.

Jack had two vehicles at that time. He owned a nice "Grandpa" car, a big four door sedan that was low and comfy and felt like you were riding down the road in your living room. For this evening, he chose to drive his big Dodge Ram pickup truck. He was sitting behind the wheel impatiently waiting for me to get off the sidewalk, cross in front of his truck, and open the passenger side door to get in. When I finally opened the door the dome light came on. The seat was littered with McDonald's wrappers, old newspapers, coffee cups, etc. "Oh. Hold on," he said, obviously annoyed. With a grand sweeping of his right arm, all the debris made its way to the floor in front of the passenger seat. I tossed my clutch up onto the seat, hoisted my dress up to my wazoo, and grabbed the handle attached to the inside frame to lob myself upward into the cab. WHEW! Good thing I'm flexible.

And down the road we went. No chit-chat. No "How's your day been so far? Are you having a good birthday?" Instead, Jack flipped the radio to a talk show about politics. Personally, I prefer to listen to music, and I don't like to debate politics but, hey, it was his truck. The driver gets to pick what plays on the radio, right? For the next 25 minutes we listened to the radio host give his opinions on the political climate of the country. Then he'd argue with his guest about what changes needed to happen with the people making laws and so on. Ugh. I kept quiet and kept reminding myself of what great food they had at the restaurant we were going to that night.

We finally arrived at the restaurant and, yes, there was still a light coating of snow on the ground. Jack jumped out of his truck and headed toward the door. I barely had my door open and was trying to gracefully hit the ground without doing a split (I'm not THAT flexible). Once I managed that feat, I headed toward the door where he'd already gone inside. He was certainly in a mood, and I didn't know why. Maybe he'd had a rough day at work. A delicious meal and some yummy dessert would certainly lift his mood. Or so I thought. I finally tippy-tapped on my high heels into the restaurant and caught up with Jack at the hostess podium. She said, "Follow me" and led us to a nice booth in the main dining room.

Jack slid into one side of the booth as I took off my coat and placed it in the booth before me. I tucked myself in on the other side and gave him a smile, letting him know how happy I was to be there. I looked around and noticed a pretty good crowd for a Tuesday night. Lots of families were dining with us. Good thing

I called and made the reservation after all. Just then a cute young waitress of about 21 or so showed up to our table all smiles. "May I get you something from the bar?"

Jack's eyes narrowed. He looked at her like he was about to ask a question and her very life may depend on her answer. "What kind of whiskey do you carry?"

The young lady responded, "Well, we have all the regular main brands, so if you have a particular one in mind, I can check."

His brow furrowed. "WELL NOW, if you don't know what whiskeys you have on hand, are you really knowledgeable about your job?"

Uh-oh. The waitress just smiled as I'm sure she's trained to do and said she'd be right back. A minute later she came back and read off a list of at least ten different high-quality brands of whiskey. Jack ordered a double Glenfiddich on the rocks. Then the waitress looked at me and I asked for a Coors Light. I proudly exclaimed, "It's my birthday!" just like any little kid would. She nodded and off she went to fetch our beverages. She came back and put our drinks in front of us. We then ordered our meals. I ordered a moderate fish dinner, nothing too elaborate or expensive. Jack ordered a steak and sides. And another double Glenfiddich on the rocks, please.

After draining the second double, Jack decided he needed to enlighten me–and apparently everyone else in the dining room–about his political opinions. Perhaps he was still mentally involved in the radio host's earlier conversation. It's true that drunk people don't realize how loudly they're speaking. Jack started in on the state of our country. Loudly. And stabbing his left index finger in the air with each point made. "WELL YA KNOW WHAT THOSE FUCKIN' POLITICIANS NEED? THEY ALL NEED A GOOD FUCKIN' KICK IN THEIR BALLS! THEY'RE A BUNCH OF FUCKIN' LOSERS WHO ARE FUCKIN' UP OUR COUNTRY SO FUCKIN' BAD!"

I could feel my face and neck go crimson. I felt my shoulders and upper body folding in as I tried to make myself disappear in the booth. I looked around. All eyes were on us. I scooched down in the booth a little and put my right hand up to the side of my face as if I could hide. I tried to change the subject a few times in a much lower voice but guess what happened?

"YOU GOTTA BE AWARE OF WHAT THESE ASSHOLES ARE

DOING! YOU GOTTA MAKE SURE YOU VOTE AND YOU GOTTA GET THE FUCKIN' IDIOTS OUT OF OFFICE BEFORE THEY RUIN US! WE'RE TAXPAYERS GODDAMMIT! THEY CAN'T FUCK US OVER FOREVER IF WE STAND UP TO THEM!"

Sweet Jesus. Thankfully the meal came at that moment, and we ate in silence. That is, after he ordered his third double whiskey. It was at this point that he reached into his pants pocket and pulled out his truck keys. He tossed them over to me, barely missing my plate, and said, "Here, you're driving back tonight." No kidding. Trying to salvage something of the evening, I made comments on how delicious my dinner was and how lovely it was plated. That's when Jack had eaten enough of his dinner and decided to carry on with his lecture on politics.

His baritone voice reverberated off the walls. "WHAT THOSE RETARDS NEED IS A GOOD DOSE OF REALITY! THEY DON'T KNOW WHAT THE REGULAR FUCKING JOE GOES THROUGH EVERY DAY TO PAY HIS FUCKING BILLS!"

I was trying to eat as fast as I could so we could get out of there. He'd only eaten half of his dinner but managed to flag down our waitress for, yes, number four of the double whiskey. I finally finished my meal which had my belly hurting from wolfing it too fast. The poor little waitress came over and practically threw the check on the table. She didn't ask if we wanted coffee or dessert. No upsell at the end of our meal. I'm sure enough people complained, and the manager told her to get us the Hell out of there. Jack reached over, making a big display of picking up the dinner check. He looked at me through his glassy, dazed eyes and said, "Don't worry. It's your birthday. I got this." Then he proceeded to get up, put his jacket on and walk away. I slunk out of the booth, put on my coat, and headed toward the door hoping nobody in the restaurant recognized me. I didn't make eye contact with anyone. I was mesmerized by the carpet on the floor.

When I finally caught up with him at the truck, he was annoyed that I took so long to get out there and unlock it for him. I pole-vaulted up behind the wheel and adjusted the seat and mirrors. I said, "Okay, let's head back to my place and chill out for the night."

That's when Jack looked at me and said, "We gotta stop at my place first. I gotta pick up my kit." Hmmm. He knew he'd be spending the night at my house but didn't think to pack his overnight bag? No toothbrush, no jammie pants or t-shirt to bum around in? Well, okay. Maybe he just forgot. Off we went, out of our way, to his house.

We arrived at Jack's house, went inside and the first thing he did was grab a beer out of the fridge. "Want one?" he asked.

I feigned a smile and said, "No thanks, I'm still stuffed from dinner." Jack then proceeded to pound down two Labatt Blues while putting his stuff in a duffel bag. Back to the big truck we went.

As I was pulling out of his driveway and down the street, he said, "Hey, take me over to my buddy's store. I wanna show him how pretty you are tonight." This confused me. I wasn't following his logic at all. His friend owned a small convenience store in town. We didn't need anything more at my place, but I thought, okay. He's trying to say he appreciates how nice I look. I drove to the store, and we went inside. "HEY DICKY! HEY DICKY! LOOK AT MY GIRLFRIEND! DOESN'T SHE LOOK HOT?" The slurred words tumbled out of Jack's whiskey-numbed mouth.

Dicky stood behind the counter in his customer-less store. He could easily tell his friend Jack was a bit shitfaced. Dicky smiled at me. "Yeah, Jack, she looks really nice." I gave Dicky a weak smile and a slight nod to acknowledge his compliment.

"YEAH! IT'S HER FUCKIN' BIRTHDAY SO I JUST TREATED HER TO A REALLY FUCKIN' GOOD DINNER AND I TIPPED THE WAITRESS SO GOOD SHE'LL NEVER FORGET ME!" The words tripped over his alcohol-numbed tongue. Ummm . . . I'm sure she'll never forget you but it's probably not for the tip. Dicky then offered Jack a beer and he accepted.

Dicky offered me one, and again I smiled and politely said, "No thanks, I'm driving tonight."

"DICKY! WHEN IS THAT COMPUTER GEEK KID OF YOURS GONNA COME OVER AND FIX MY DESKTOP? I CAN'T GET THAT PARIS HILTON VIDEO TO PLAY. AND I WANNA SEE IT! I HEAR SHE TAKES IT UP THE ASS! YEAH, MAN, I WANNA SEE PARIS HILTON GETTING BONED UP THE FUCKIN' ASS!"

Right about then I was pretty much in shock. Not that I haven't worked around men before and not that I haven't heard rough language. It was the context, the attitude, the volume. Dicky didn't know what to say. Jack turned to me and asked, "What's YOUR problem? Oh, I know. You're SUCH a prude!" Wow. By this time, I was wondering if maybe there's such a thing as a world record for the worst date ever and how would I spend the prize money. Dicky told Jack he'd send his tech-smart son over the next weekend to look at his computer.

Jack finally finished his beer and said it was time to go. Dicky had customers to wait on by then and I was grateful. We hiked up into the Dodge and finally headed to my house. I wasn't talking because, honestly, I was speechless. Jack looked over to me and asked, "What's YOUR problem?"

As calmly as I could, I turned to him and said, "Gee, Jack. I don't know. Maybe I just thought it was inappropriate to be talking with your buddy about wanting to watch another woman get it up the ass while we're on a date for MY birthday?"

He rolled his big glossy blue eyes and hissed, "You are SUCH a fuckin' PRUDE!"

Silence.

The next fifteen minutes were bliss. He was in the passenger seat bobbing and weaving. I finally pulled into my driveway. I turned the truck off, pulled the keys, and put them in the cup holder like he always did. I lowered myself to the driveway, onto my snowy sidewalk and then turned around to see if he needed help getting into the house. Jack had exited the passenger side of his truck just fine and was rounding the front of the vehicle. Then he made an abrupt left and was getting behind the wheel. No. NOT good. I shuffled back to the truck and opened the driver's door. Quietly and kindly I said, "C'mon Jack. Come inside. You can't drive home like this." Many years ago, I lost a brother to a drunk driver. This is a very sensitive topic for me. I don't want ANYONE to drive drunk.

Again, Jack bared his teeth and replied, "AHHHH, FUCK YOU! I'M FINE!" and he slammed the door, cranked the engine, dropped the shifting lever into reverse, and headed down my driveway. Nothing I could do to stop him, so I headed toward the door. That's when it hit me: I didn't have my house key. I knew Jack had a key to my house on his key ring, so I didn't bother putting my bulky keyring in my tiny purse. There I was, mid-November, standing outside my house in a short dress and heels. Snowing. Cold. And I was in the country. After saying some not-so-ladylike words to myself, I trudged in the now ankle-deep snow to my back door. Yup. I locked it as I always do. Part of me was hoping I'd forgotten to lock it, but I knew better.

I then shuffled to the back of the house, off the sidewalk. The still soft, yet snow-covered, grass allowed my heels to sink in about an inch or so. I decided to try all my windows. Sure enough, one of my dining room windows on the back of the house didn't have a latch on it. I just hadn't gotten around to fixing it yet, thankfully. I palmed the glass and shimmied the window open about a foot. I tossed my small purse and high heels inside. I stood there in the snow in my little black dress and stockings. Then I laid my coat on the windowsill, placed my hands firmly on it, bent my knees, and jumped and pulled for all I was worth. Fortunately, I was in pretty good shape for a forty-two-year-old and my upper body strength was enough to pull me as far as my boobs to the inside of the windowsill. Wiggling, kicking, pushing, and pulling like a baby alpaca being born, I made my way inside and dropped onto my dining room floor. SAFE.

I closed the window. I trotted to the bedroom, undressed, put my jammies on, headed to the bathroom to take off my makeup. Then I sat on my living room couch and proceeded to cry. What happened? What was tonight all about? What did I say or do that ticked Jack off so much that he felt he had to derail the evening at every turn? I went over and over every detail of the days leading up to my birthday and to the evening itself. I could NOT for the life of me figure out what had gotten him so spun up that he'd wreck my birthday so badly. I finally went to bed as bewildered as could be.

No word from Jack the next day, so I went over to his house while he was at work. I went in, laid his house key on the table and left a note. I said I didn't know what last night was all about, but it was obvious he didn't want to be with me, as he did his best to make it a miserable evening.

Two days later I couldn't take it anymore. I had to know. I called him. After calmly pleading with him to tell me what was wrong, he finally caved. And that's when he told me the truth. Apparently when I told him I wanted to go to dinner, he was fine with that. BUT, I said I'd like to have him spend the night with me. That's where "I" screwed up. Now mind you, we'd spent many nights in the previous couple of months or so at his house. We weren't shy with each other physically. For my peace of mind, I once more asked him to tell me what was the problem. A little bit of heavy breathing and obvious frustration was all I could hear at the other end of the telephone line. Then, "I'LL TELL YOU WHAT THE PROBLEM IS! YOU SAID YOU WANTED ME TO SPEND THE NIGHT. DO YOU HAVE ANY IDEA HOW MUCH PRESSURE THAT PUTS ON A GUY? KNOWING HE'LL HAVE TO PERFORM SEXUALLY? I DIDN'T LIKE HOW YOU JUST EXPECTED THAT I'D WANT TO HAVE SEX THAT NIGHT!"

For about the fiftieth time in three days, I was speechless. Because it was implied or assumed that we would make love, have sex, get down and dirty, knock boots or whatever you want to call it, he felt pressured? This was a first for me. Most men must beg for it, right? Most men will take it anywhere, anytime. They aren't picky. Here was a guaranteed thing and he felt . . . pressured. He was a fit and healthy man with no restrictions or physical problems. I couldn't understand what was so horrible about me being a "win" for him that night. I'm still confused to this day.

A few days later I stopped at a gas station not far from Jack's house. I went inside to pay for my gas and right there near the cash register was a small rack of generic cards. Birthday, sympathy, blank ones. They were right next to the box of hand warmers. Cards: fifty cents each. Hand warmers: One dollar per two-pack.

Fast forward eighteen years later. I'm still single. My picker's broken. Badly. And Jack's still single. Not surprisingly. I guess some of us are destined to be single for one reason or another. I've had a few bad birthdays since then, but none can even come close to my 42nd disaster.

COOKIES

This isn't a story. It's my favorite chocolate chip cookie recipe that I've made for years. Out of all the things I bake, this is the most requested item. Follow the directions and use the right ingredients, and you'll have the perfect cookie!

Cream together:
1 ½ cups (3 sticks) of soft, unsalted butter
1   cup of light brown sugar
½   cup sugar

Add:
1   large box (family size) of instant vanilla pudding
1 ½ teaspoons pure vanilla extract
3   eggs

Then:
3 ⅓ cups of flour
1 ⅕ teaspoons of baking soda
3   cups of semi-sweet chocolate chips

If you have the time, refrigerate the dough for an hour or more before baking. NOT imperative, but it does help keep the cookies from spreading. Drop onto a cookie sheet and bake at 365°F for 8-10 minutes.

Helpful hints:
Do NOT overbake. Take them out of the oven when they still look soft and slightly glossy in the middle, but the edges are a light tan. Let the cookies sit for 5 minutes before removing to a wire rack to cool. Switch up the pudding and chips: use chocolate pudding with peanut butter chips. Try butterscotch pudding and chips. White chips work with everything. Mix and match. Use REAL butter and REAL vanilla. Seriously, this makes a difference. Sprinkle coarse sea salt on top before baking for an

extra zing (but make sure you eat the cookies upside down, the top of the cookie hitting your tongue first).

MICKEY'S GIFT

"What do you think it is?"

"The wiggly lines."

"How about this one?"

"A star."

"And this one?"

"A circle."

The deck of cards she had wasn't like any other I'd ever seen before. They had silly designs on them, not numbers or faces of kings or queens. There were no diamonds, clubs, hearts, or spades. She would shuffle the deck then hold the cards up one by one with the face toward her and the back toward me. I had to guess what was on the card. It could be a circle, a star, three squiggly lines, a square, or a plus sign. These cards were designed to test and hone one's psychic abilities. As a child, I just thought it was fun to get some one-on-one time alone with my mother. She did this card game with all of us kids. When I look back on it, I seem to recall I was the only one out of us six kids who wanted to play it as much as I could. I was drawn to them. When my mother was busy, I'd take her cards and scatter them face down on the table and pick one up at random, guess what it was, then turn it over. I'd keep the ones I'd guessed correctly on the right side of me, the ones I missed on the left. Seems the more I played, the bigger the pile on my right became. Now and then I'd catch my mother watching me as she went about her household chores. She'd just smile and nod and tell me to keep going. Little did I know, she was encouraging me to explore my own mind, to stretch the limits that society had placed on all of us.

Back in the 1960's it wasn't fashionable to be interested in ESP, life after death, spirits, haunted houses, déjà vu, and so on. It was considered Devil worship, toying with demons, and just asking to be possessed by evil spirits. My mother was definitely ahead of her time. Oh, how she'd have relished the sudden interest in life after death shown on today's television shows. The ghost hunters, the séances, the psychics who really do baffle people with personal knowledge they can uncover. She'd have been totally pissed at the obvious frauds and charlatans bilking people out of their hard-earned money. On the other hand, she'd have been sitting on the edge of her seat when a plausible person was explaining what they were doing to contact the spirits.

Marilyn, also known as Mick, Mickey, and of course Ma, sharpened her psychic talents throughout the years even though she was mocked, put down, ridiculed, and criticized. Her passion for the unknown, the unexplainable, was never-ending. She wasn't just interested in the great beyond. She hungered to know what was next. Mickey didn't believe that once you died, that was it. She was raised Methodist so the idea of being a good person and going to Heaven had been instilled in her since she was a child. Likewise, she knew being bad guaranteed a spot in Hell with the Devil himself torturing you for all eternity. But what about all those odd things that she'd experienced? What about all those people who were legally and medically declared dead but came back and described the afterlife? Mickey needed to know, so she read. She studied. She asked questions of ministers, priests, rabbis, and anyone who had greater knowledge of the afterlife. "We pray to the Father, Son, and Holy GHOST, don't we?" would be one of her first questions. So why do so many people deny the possibility of ghosts? We say our spirit leaves us when we die, so we DO have spirits, right? A soul? Our essence?

As I said, my mother was gifted. A couple of examples for you. Many years ago, my folks were looking for a farm. They had toured several farms in the area they wanted to settle in, and this one in particular stood out. As the real estate agent and my parents were walking toward a large hay barn with the door open, my mother stood there staring up at a broad wooden beam that stretched the width of the barn. She was frozen in the big doorway just fixated on that beam. The agent turned and asked her if she wanted to come in and see the rest of the barn. Without thinking, my mother asked, "Who hanged himself here?" She pointed to that beam with her shaky hand. The agent was silent. My father never said a word. My mother asked again. "Who hanged himself from that beam, right there?" The agent became flustered and asked who told her about it. Nobody. Back then you didn't have to reveal suicides or murders. My mother could "SEE" a man hanging there and felt the coldness in that doorway, even though it was summertime. Mickey looked at my father and said, "No. We are NOT buying this farm," and she turned and slowly walked back to the car and slid into the back seat, ready to leave.

My mother used to read cards, use the Ouija board and pendulum, hold séances, visit cemeteries, and sometimes go to houses that people claimed were haunted. On the occasions she took us kids, we'd all sit or play quietly in the living room as my mother visited with her friends in the kitchen. They always gave my mother a tour of their home first, then they'd settle in the kitchen for a chat. We just thought she was having coffee with people she enjoyed. We didn't know what was really going on because we were too young to understand. Again, many years later it all clicked, especially for me. Several times I remember leaving these places and after we were home for a bit, my mother would pull me aside and ask me what I thought of her friend's house. Sometimes I'd say it was pretty, or very cluttered. Other times I'd tell her about the cold spot in the living room where we were allowed to hang out. Or I'd tell her about that shadow that I saw go through the dining room. We had a way of talking about this stuff without really talking about it, if you know what I mean. She didn't want me to get spooked, but she did want to sharpen my skills. Years later we laughed about how sly and cagey she was with me.

Mickey's talents became known in the Brasher area not long after we moved up here in 1974. She couldn't and wouldn't hide her fascination with the afterlife or psychic phenomenon. Some people loved coming to visit her. Others mocked her and put her down. She didn't care about the second crowd. She knew she had an unappreciated passion for the unknown. And the unknown makes people uneasy. I remember getting teased in school about my mother and what the other kids assumed our home life must have been like. Kids can be cruel and that's taught by their parents. I vividly remember a kid asking me if my mother wore a tall, black, pointy hat. He also asked if we sacrificed chickens and drank their blood. Another kid told me

I was going to be tortured by Satan because my mother was a witch. Wow.

And yet the people still came around to get their cards read, to use the Ouija board, or to see if my mother could pick up on any spirits with messages for them. My father was NOT a fan of my mother's hobby. He just wanted a regular housewife. Sorry, Oscar. Not gonna happen. Even I went through my selfish stage where I wanted a "normal" mom. I didn't want to be taunted at school for having a weird mother. Eventually I adopted her attitude and just let people think what they wanted. What's that popular saying? Other people's opinion of you is none of your business. So true.

And now here I am, nowhere near as talented as my mother was, but certainly still learning, still honing my skills, and always interested in the afterlife, ESP, intuition, etc. I find it all fascinating and have plenty of stories of my own. I have friends and acquaintances who can vouch for a few of my "out there" moments. I've definitely inherited many things from my mother. And I'm not complaining.

CABBAGE ROLLS

This story is one that makes me (and a few others) laugh every time the words "cabbage rolls" are spoken or read.

Many years ago, I owned a few rental properties. Most of my tenants ended up being my friends. Over the years, I was lucky enough to enjoy many of the people who rented from me. Oh sure, I had enough headaches with the tenants from Hell, too. But the ones who were friendly, clean, and paid their rent on time were blessings whom I cherished. Tenants like that are real treasures and, believe me, it broke my heart when the good ones bought their own houses and moved out of my properties.

Early one summer afternoon I stopped in at one of my apartments to pick up the rent from my tenant, Cindy. She was an older lady living on a fixed income. Cindy was always happy and cheerful with such a good outlook on life. If I hadn't been on my way into work that afternoon, I would have gladly had a cold beer with her on the side porch of the apartment house. I had to get going, so she handed me the rent check, and out the door I went. She came scrambling down the porch steps after me and said, "Pendra! Wait! I made cabbage rolls, so take some into work for your supper tonight." She handed me a Cool-Whip bowl that was still warm. I smiled and humbly thanked her for her generosity. I never had the heart to say "no" to her when she offered food because I knew that was her way of expressing love. I totally get it. I do the same thing. However, I'm not a big fan of cabbage rolls. Never have been. I've never felt the big woo-hoo when people say they're having cabbage rolls for dinner. Cindy had a heart as big as the great outdoors, so I was polite, thanked her very much, and headed into work.

When I got to my job, I tossed the Cool-Whip bowl into the fridge down in the turbine gallery where I was scheduled to work that evening. I went about my business of getting readings on the generators, doing inspections and other routine tasks my job entailed. I'd totally forgotten about the cabbage rolls I'd put in the fridge because I'd packed my own dinner and ate that. I finished my shift at 10:30 p.m. and went home.

The next day I had to work a double shift: day shift, which was from 6:30 a.m. until 2:30 p.m. and then stay for the afternoon shift from 2:30 p.m. until 10:30 p.m. I got up early, showered, packed up my lunch and supper for the day, and headed into work. Again, I was scheduled for the turbine gallery duties, so I headed down there when I arrived on site. The usual routine of starting the units, taking readings, and doing clearances on switchgears, pumps, or whatever needed to be done, kept me busy for most of the morning. At around 11:00 a.m. one of the laborers came into the office.

This laborer was affectionately known as "3kB." (More on that in a minute.) His name was Bill, and he was quite the character. Bill stood at least 6'2" tall. He was handsome, lean and lanky, and held the best posture I've ever seen on a human. Bill's straight light brown hair was almost a retro-70's hairstyle, but it worked perfectly for him. His bright eyes danced whenever he'd tell a joke or if he knew he was getting the better of you. Now and then he'd stroke his well-kept beard as he pondered what he'd do with the millions he was sure he'd win on the next lottery draw. His laugh was infectious. Bill's knowledge of current events, world affairs, and trivia were matched by none. Conversations with him would have you thinking, arguing (with him "winning" most of the time because of his knack for remembering facts), laughing, and just wishing you didn't have to return to work. Bill's sense of humor would have you rolling within minutes. His best stories were the true events that had happened to him in his life: "Hey, did I ever tell you about the time I got shot with an arrow?"

We had dubbed Bill "3kB" because he was an entrepreneur and wanted to start a soft-serve ice cream stand in his hometown. He approached several of us about investing "Just $3,000" in his new business. Unfortunately, the timing wasn't good for most of us. We all had mortgages, car payments, college loans, children, and so on. We appreciated the opportunity to get in on his business but, in the end, none of us could spare $3,000 at that time. He was extremely gracious about it and was never bitter that we couldn't back his endeavor. In the end, he did find the funds to open his shop and it was a thriving business. Way to go, Bill!

Back to that day. Bill walked into the office around 11:00 a.m. to empty the wastepaper basket and sweep and mop the floor. It was almost a dance when he came in because we'd automatically get out of his way and let him do his job. I grabbed my logbook which I was filling out when he first came in and moved off to the opposite side of the desk to give him room to work. We started chatting about this and that and he mentioned how he'd overslept that morning and barely had time to jump into his work boots and get to the job by 7:00 a.m. He sighed and said he'd have to hit up the vending machine for lunch in half an hour. I then remembered the cabbage rolls Cindy had given me the previous afternoon.

"Bill, do you like cabbage rolls?" I asked.

"Babycakes, I fuckin' LOVE cabbage rolls!" He was always coming up with funny nicknames, so I was Babycakes that day.

"Well, Bill, I have some cabbage rolls in the fridge. BUT, I'll give you a heads-up, I didn't make them. One of my tenants gave them to me yesterday and honestly, I'm not a big fan. I didn't want to hurt her feelings, so I took them when she handed them to me. They're yours if you want them."

"Oh my God! Seriously? You don't want them?" Bill's eyes lit up and he was smiling.

"Seriously. I do NOT want them. Let me grab them for you." I got up and went out to the fridge, pulled out the Cool-

Whip tub and brought it back into the office. I handed it to him and the delight on his face was so precious.

"Ohhh, THANK YOU, Babycakes! You just saved Ol' Billy Ray from starvation today!" And off he went, like this was the day he'd finally won the lottery.

About an hour later I was sitting in the office when Bill came to the door and opened it. He slowly closed the door behind him, leaving the noise of the turbine gallery outside. He stood there, tall and straight. Shoulders squared, a serious look on his face. For a moment I thought maybe someone had just died and I hadn't heard the news yet.

"Bill, you ok?" I asked.

"No. No, Babycakes, I'm not ok."

"What's wrong?" My concern was starting to crawl upwards.

"Wrong? I'll tell you what's wrong." The serious tone in Bill's voice had me worried. His body language told me he wasn't happy, that something was definitely not right. I sat there quietly, waiting for him to continue.

Bill softly said to me, "Now, I don't mean to sound ungrateful, but do you know what was in those cabbage rolls?"

"No, Bill. I told you I didn't make them. I told you my tenant did, but I didn't eat any, so I have no idea. Why?"

"WHY? I'll tell you why. You wanna know what was in them? I'll tell you what was in them." By now I'm starting to laugh a little bit because of the relief that it wasn't anything life-threatening. It was just about those freakin' cabbage rolls. And I knew Bill's sense of humor, so I sat there waiting.

"I'll tell you what she put in them." His voice level had raised a little bit. Then it got a little louder, and as he stood there, pillar-straight, he told me. "FUCKIN'" (his bearded chin jutting out toward me) "CANNED" (his chin jutting again, jabbing the air between us) "HASH" (his chin stabbing the air)!

I lost it. I started laughing. I couldn't help it. I can't say if it was the fact that my tenant had used that god-awful canned hash as filler for the cabbage rolls, or if it was the physical movement, the total emphasis of each word using his chin that made me roar.

"Babycakes! This shit isn't funny. Most people cook up some hamburger, spices, add in some rice, and wrap it all up in a cabbage leaf and put sauce on it. That's what cabbage rolls are, right? But not this lady. No. She used FUCKIN' (chin) CANNED (chin) HASH (chin)!"

The more I laughed, the worse it got. I apologized to Bill several times, but I had to remind him that I hadn't made the cabbage rolls and that he was on his own with them. He finally calmed down enough and started laughing too. He admitted it was his own fault for taking food from a stranger and, in the end, he didn't blame me. We had a good chuckle out of it, and we carried on with the rest of our day. After that, every now and then we'd see each other at work, and I'd tell him I had some food for him from Cindy. He'd put his hands up and give me a very colorful description of what I could do with it. Such a great sense of humor. Word got out about the cabbage roll incident, and eventually people would tell me about the Methodist church having a cabbage roll sale, or there would be some fundraiser selling them or whatever. People would put these notices on my locker or on the janitor's closet so Bill could see them. All in good fun, of course.

A few years went by and, sadly enough, Bill passed away. He was way too young. When word of his death spread through the workplace, a heaviness was felt by all of us. His humor and wit were missed by everyone.

It's been many years now since we lost Bill. Occasionally I'll drive by one of the local churches and see their sign advertising cabbage rolls for sale or a cabbage roll supper being held. I always smile and say, "Hi Bill!" If I think of it, I'll send a Facebook message to his daughter and let her know I was thinking of that crazy guy. I believe it's important to let family members know they're not alone in their grief and when someone is missed.

And the story still goes on. A couple of weeks ago I met up

with a few of my fellow retirees. We were sitting at a diner for breakfast and as we all scoped out the menu, we were tossing suggestions out there. One guy said, "Oh, look, a meat lover's omelet. That looks good."

Another guy said, "Man, I could destroy a pile of pancakes this morning."

I glanced at my former workmate sitting across from me, and he was slowly looking up from his menu. He had a wicked smirk on his face. I cocked my head to one side and asked, "What's so funny?"

This is the guy who is usually quiet, and he said, "They have an omelet here . . . and it has hash in it." That's all he said, but his eyes were twinkling, and he was smiling ear to ear.

Before I could say anything, the other two guys asked in unison, "FUCKIN' CANNED HASH?"

It's a good thing there weren't too many people in the diner at that moment. We might have been asked to leave because of the loud laughter. When we finally stopped laughing, we all raised our coffee mugs and toasted 3kB. He will never be forgotten.

But wait! There's more!

At that breakfast with my former workmates, I mentioned I was writing a book about a variety of incidents and people in my life. One of the guys, Murray Armstrong, was the one who suggested I add in the cabbage roll story. And he was right. It's a story worth telling because even after all these years, it still brings laughter into our lives. We lost Bill seventeen years ago, but his humor lives on.

A week or so later, Murray told me he had a story about Bill he'd like to share. A little backstory here: Murray is a big guy, standing well over six feet tall. Back then he was very much into weightlifting and bodybuilding. His biceps were about as big as an aged oak tree. His shoulders were wide enough to block doorways (okay, minor exaggeration, but not by much). Murray was known for his dedication to his bodybuilding, and he took all the ribbing we dished out with a smile. One day Bill walked into the office in the turbine gallery and began chatting with Murray. Just out of curiosity, Bill asked Murray how much weight he could bench press. Murray thought for a second, then told Bill his current bench press was 370 pounds. When Bill heard that, he tilted his head back, looked at the ceiling and in his loudest voice exclaimed, "MURRAY IS MY FRIEND!" Murray said he just started laughing. Was Bill telling God? Or was he telling everyone else out there in the big, scary world that he has this monster of a friend who can bench 370 pounds? Surely Bill wanted to stay on Murray's good side. Thank you, Murray, for sharing this one. I'm sure anyone who knew Bill is picturing him right now.

OLD FOLKS AND PENNIES

A few more stories from a beloved elder are the ones about pennies and more. Winnifred, known as Winnie to everyone who knew and loved her, was a grand ninety-three years old when she passed. She'd lived a good, long, fulfilling life as a farmer's wife. Mother to four, grandmother and great-grandmother to many. Winnie had to be one of the hardest working women I'd ever had the honor to meet. Standing at a mere five-feet-two inches tall and built like a fire hydrant, she was as sturdy as they came. Her gray hair had evolved to white by the time she turned eight-five. She looked like a stocky cotton swab. Her dark brown eyes of youth had faded to a light chocolate color but still gleamed with intelligence and passion.

I was visiting Winnie one afternoon and that's when we started talking about good luck charms. As you know, I'm a little superstitious and sometimes I think, "Well, it can't hurt to try it" when it comes to obtaining good luck. We've all had bad luck and we've all enjoyed good luck. Who doesn't want the latter? I sat in Winnie's living room nibbling on some lemon cookies she'd baked that morning and asked her to enlighten me. I wanted to know what kind of good luck charms or rituals I could try.

"Honey, the first thing you need is a good man." Winnie stated this as a stone-cold fact of life. She knew I was single and that my picker was broken. My dating life was a disaster, and this bothered her. Winnie had married at the ripe old age of eighteen and widowed at eighty-seven. Not a bad run in this day and age.

I smiled at her and asked, "Okay, just how on earth am I going to get one?"

"I have a few ideas." Winnie said as an absolute statement. Confidence was something she never lacked. Looking me squarely in the eyes, she said, "You should take notes. I have a few good ideas that just might help you." And then she proceeded to give me a pad of paper and a pen. How could I refuse?

She leaned back in her big, overstuffed chair and took a deep breath. With her soft eyes on me, she gave the following list: "Number one. Take two shiny pennies and tape them to the back of your headboard. Every night when you go to sleep, touch your headboard behind your pillow and ask God to send your husband soon."

I smiled. And I wrote. I was amused because I'm not much of a "God" person. As cliché as it sounds, I'm NOT religious, but I am spiritual. I believe in my loved ones who have gone before me. When I pray, I pray to them and ask for their help. I try to be a good person to everyone. I may not be successful all the time, but I do try and that should count for something. The other thing I smiled about was the "husband" part. Winnie didn't say ask God for a good man, boyfriend, companion. No. She said husband. Apparently, we don't need to watch the whole movie, just fast forward to the last five minutes where the girl gets the guy, and the rice is thrown. Winnie leaned forward to pick up her cup of tea and a cookie. After a sip and a bite, she cocked her head and said, "As long as we're on the subject of pennies, don't forget to put a penny, heads up, in your shoes. If you want a husband, put one in your left shoe. If you want money and health, put one in your right one." I furiously scribbled her directions. Right: money and health. Left: man. Got it.

"Never underestimate the power of the penny!" She grinned and polished off her cookie, took another sip of tea then continued. "If you want a happy home, tuck a penny in each room of your house. You can put one on top of the highest cupboard in the kitchen, so nobody takes it. You can slip one under the sofa in the living room. Put one under the sink in the bathroom. You get it. Just put them all over your house where nobody will see them or pick them up for you. And, of course, make sure they're heads up and the shinier the better!" I duly noted her instructions. All rooms. Heads up. Shiny.

"Number three!" Winnie declared as she cleared her throat. "Bake fresh bread once a week, if not more. The smell will get out there in the universe and your husband will smell that divine scent and come running to you."

Hmmm. Fresh bread as a good luck charm? I am SO in! Hell, I might just be happy alone if I have enough freshly baked bread on hand. But Winnie insisted that no man could resist the smell and taste of bread. "And make sure it's a good yeast bread, one that you have to let rise at least twice. None of that store-boughten box stuff that tastes like cardboard. That won't get you a good man. That'll get you heartache for sure."

Her seriousness amused me. She took this stuff to heart and by this time, I was starting to also. Her tone was so convincing.

"That's enough for now as far as the husband catching goes," she stated. "Just you try those for now and if they don't work, come back and we'll go over a few more ideas." My beloved Winnie. She had the biggest, most loving heart of anyone I've ever known.

"On to other good luck charms!" You'd have thought she was giving a lecture on brain surgery. She was that serious. "When you're out in your garden or if you're working on houseplants, don't forget to spit in the dirt. Mother Nature likes it when you have some of yourself invested in the job. Now, don't be spitting all day. That's just nasty. But when you're planting your vegetables or tending to your flowers, spit at the beginning of each row. If you put a stake or marker down for each row of seeds, spit near the marker. That's good enough. And don't forget to cover it up with a little dirt."

I helped myself to another cookie because, really, who

could ever get enough of Winnie's lemon cookies? They really hit the spot and who am I to refuse her generosity? Okay, okay. They're delicious and I made a damned pig out of myself. Happy now?

"How's your car running?" was her next question.

I thought about it and replied, "It's running fine. I get the oil changed when it needs it, keep the wiper fluid topped off, and occasionally check the air in the tires."

"I'll tell you this much, youngster. I drove a vehicle up until I turned eighty years old. I didn't want to stop driving, but I knew it was probably time. I know I'm not as fast as before and I'd never forgive myself if I caused harm to anyone else. In all those years of driving, I never once had an accident. Not even a fender bender. No sliding off the road in the winter, no falling asleep at the wheel. Not even a parking ticket. Do you know why?" Her eyes twinkled as she waited for my obvious response.

"No. I don't know why." I replied.

Winnie slapped her hand on the arm of her chair and exclaimed, "It was the PENCIL!" as if that was all the explanation I needed. I believe the confused look on my face delighted her.

"Umm . . . the pencil?" I asked as I jotted this down on my pad.

"Of course, it was the pencil. Always put a pencil in your car. Put it anywhere. Leave it in there for as long as you own that car. When you trade or sell that car, take the pencil out and put it in your next car. If you forget it in your old car, that's all right. It'll just help the new owners. But make damned sure you put another pencil in your new car. That pencil is writing your driving story. We all want a good, safe driving story. So put a pencil in your car. Always!"

I could see Winnie was looking a little tired at this time, so I looked at my watch and told her I really had to get going, but could we resume this chat another time? She was delighted to say yes. What an absolute treasure this lady was. Winnie was the grandmother I never had. I feel absolutely blessed to have met her and to have had her in my life.

Now, you're probably wondering if I followed through on any of her suggestions. I'll confess right here that I have not taped two shiny pennies to the back of my headboard. At this moment in my life, I'm not sure I want a husband. I wonder if taping just one penny will be enough to get me a decent boyfriend. Maybe I'll try that.

I do have a couple pairs of shoes with pennies in the right one. Is it just coincidence that I had a great job with a wonderful retirement package? Maybe. However, a shiny penny is still tucked under my favorite, most comfortable pair of steel-toed work boots that I wore on my job for years before I retired.

If you come to my house, you won't see any pennies (heads up! shiny!) anywhere. But they're there. In every room.

I do bake bread now and then, but not on a weekly basis. Again, same with the two pennies on the headboard, I'm not sure if I'm ready for that yet.

If you do visit me, you'll notice how vibrant and huge my houseplants are these days. You know why.

The last vehicle I bought was in 2016 and yes, there is a pencil riding in there with me. NOT to jinx myself, but in the five, almost six years that I've owned this vehicle, I have not received any tickets, nor have I had any accidents. I did manage to put a minor scratch in the front fender shortly after I bought it because I miscalculated where my garbage wheelies were placed just outside my garage. Now that I think of it, I don't think I had a pencil in my car yet. It was that new.

Please go ahead and try some of these good luck charms and rituals. I'd be curious to see if they work for you. Winnie swore by them. And who am I to argue with Winnifred MacIntosh McDonald?

MORE SUPERSTITIONS

I try to be a good listener. Sometimes I'm successful. Other times, not so much. I went through a streak several years ago that I asked people about their superstitions. I know I'm not the only one who follows some silly rules, stories, guidelines, or whatever you want to call them for good luck or some sort of protection. I do get a kick out of people who laugh at superstitions and then later adopt a couple . . . just in case. Here's a few I gleaned from some people along the way:

1.   At big dinner functions, always set one plate extra at the table. It's for those who have passed. It's to let them know you still welcome them at your table and hope they'll bless everyone with continued love and happiness.

2.   Never put shoes on a table, even brand-new ones from the store. It's bad luck to put shoes on a table. Put them on the chair or a bench, but never on the table.

3.   Never place anything on a bible. Not even a pad of paper or a pen. The only thing you can properly place on your bible is your hand but eventually you'll be taking that off.

4.   Most people I know will only pick up a penny if it's heads-up. I had an old woman tell me to pick up ALL pennies because they're ALL pennies from heaven. She said any penny is a message from

someone who is on the other side. She went on to say heads-up may mean good luck, but tails means happiness, like the wagging of a dog's tail. I had never heard that one before, so, yes, I now pick up pennies no matter heads or tails.

5. If you're walking around in the woods, take a few minutes to place your bare hand on a big tree. Just stand there and let the spirit and strength of the tree enter your body. You'll feel more at peace and have a better sense of self if you absorb the tree's energy.

6. When you get out of bed in the morning, make sure your right foot hits the floor first, hence the adage of "getting off on the right foot" that we've all heard.

7. When you get out of a rocking chair, always make sure you place a hand on it to stop the rocking motion before you walk away. If you don't, you're inviting bad spirits to have a seat.

8. If you travel, bring back a teaspoon or two of dirt from where you've been. Add that dirt to your garden to make your memories of your trips last longer.

9. When giving a book to someone as a gift, hold it in your left hand, pass it to your right hand, then hand it to the recipient. You're adding your personal enjoyment to the gift as you pass it from your left hand to your right and from your right hand into theirs.

10. If you're having trouble deciding, stand in a doorway with your back on the casing. Think about both sides of your dilemma and the answer will come to you as you're standing there.

11. If you want someone to think of you, write his or her name three times on the palm of your hand with the index finger of your other hand. Then close your fingers around your palm for a minute.

12. Always pick up heart-shaped rocks and take them home.

Place them outside but as close to your bedroom as possible for love to find its way to you.

13.   Whenever you blow out a candle, whether it's at the dinner table or just a pretty smelling one you lit around the house, always say to yourself "Thinking of you" and remember someone who has passed. You can even say their name aloud if you're comfortable doing so.

14. Singing in the shower, even at a very low volume that only you can hear, will help wash away any fear, negativity, anxiety, stress. You're opening your soul to let the bad stuff get washed down the drain.

15.   Tap your finger on the side of your glass twice before drinking your beverage. It will bring good fortune to you.

Again, I'm amused and entertained by some of these superstitions. Still, would it hurt to try any of them? Nope. I'll check out a few and see if my life improves at all. Can't hurt, right? Let me know if you try any and what the results were. Thanks.

MIDNIGHT GARDENING

Last summer I went to my beauty salon for a tune-up. My mouse-brown hair was looking too mousy. The grays were sprouting like springtime weeds in a sidewalk crack. I may be sixty, but I don't have to look ninety. Kylie, my beautician magician, put me in her seat and draped me with what I'm sure is a Superhero cape that she wears when nobody's looking. She deserves it.

In the next chair was a younger woman, I'd guess maybe thirty to thirty-five years old or so. I glanced over and noticed she had long, manicured fingernails. Her fingers held no fewer than five rings with plenty of shiny stones. I glanced down and noticed the Frye boots she told her stylist she'd just purchased last week. No, I'm not in law enforcement. Nor am I a private detective. I used to watch silly shows like *Psych*, *Monk*, and *Murder She Wrote*. (HA! A lot of you are stumped, aren't you?! Hit the Google!) The point is, I try to be observant and as Adrian Monk would say, "It's a blessing . . . and a curse."

As my gal was performing her black magic on my hair, I sat quietly (for once) because I was being nosy and eavesdropping on the young lady to my left. Actually, it wasn't really eavesdropping, as she was speaking quite loudly, and I believe that was her intention. She wanted to make sure everyone could hear what she was saying as she humble bragged about her life and then went into victim mode, complaining about how tough her life is. This is when I started to smirk because she was really entertaining when she cried about how hard it is to raise children these days. The financial aspect of it is just KILLING her husband. He'd had to pick up a part-time job just to make sure they had everything they needed. (I found out later that SHE didn't hold a job outside the home, even though her children were in school full-time.) Ms. Frye boots went on to say she had to put the latest Xbox and other electronics on layaway because there was just no way she'd be able to afford the games AND the new iPhones up front for her little darlings for Christmas. Somewhere in that conversation it came up that her children were eight and ten years old. Hmmm . . . iPhones for eight- and ten-year-olds? Interesting.

She blathered on and on about how tough it is financially and how she just didn't think they'd be able to take their week-long vacation at Disney that year. Maybe only four days, but certainly not a whole week. Meanwhile, her beautician was politely nodding and giving the appropriate uh-huhs. I know that stylist was working at least five days a week, sometimes six, and was raising a couple of children on her own. She was on her feet at least ten hours a day dealing with all sorts of entitled personalities, and always smiled while they were in her chair. How she did it is beyond me. How ANY of them do it is beyond me.

I sat there in silence as my mind drifted back to when I was a child. My parents were extremely hard workers, but there never seemed to be enough money. We lived on a small dairy farm downstate, near Albion, NY. With eight people in the family, there was always a shortage of cash. My folks did the best they could, and their resourcefulness astounds me when I think about it now. My father ran the farm, my mother ran the house. We children would help in the barn as soon as we were old enough to safely do so. We also helped in the house from an early age. I remember doing dishes while standing on a stool at the sink and learning how to fold clothes before I was school age. My mother had given birth to her sixth child by the age of twenty-eight. She didn't have the time or patience to coddle us all day long. She was wonderfully warm and loving, but she also needed to maintain some sense of order and discipline in the house if we were all going to live together harmoniously. My father worked from before the sun came up until way after it went down. Farmers don't get union wages, hours, or breaks. But farming was what he loved to do. It was his passion. And to this day, I still hear comments about what a knowledgeable herdsman he was.

Many families struggled back in the days before all the government handouts and freebies. People were expected to work and support themselves. We all did what we needed to do to survive. That's just how it was. As hard as my parents worked, things were tight now and then. Okay, more than now and then. I remember sitting around the dinner table and my mother would dish out the food to us kids. My father would help himself to his meal. I recall looking over and seeing just one small potato and maybe a little helping of vegetables on my mother's plate. She'd nonchalantly say, "I'm just not hungry tonight. I must have nibbled too much while cooking our dinner!" Then she'd laugh it off and pass the milk. Other times she'd complain about all the extra weight she was carrying and how she really needed to diet for a week or two to get those extra pounds off her belly. She never looked fat to me. It was only years later that I realized what she was doing. It was like getting sucker punched in the gut. She was just as hungry as the rest of us. She wasn't fat, weighing about one hundred and thirty pounds. But she was a mother making sure her kids had enough to eat.

That brings me to the title of this entertaining story. My parents were very proud people. They didn't want anything they didn't earn themselves, but sometimes situations are out of our hands. That's when you must put your pride aside and do what you have to do. And with my parents, that was . . . midnight gardening.

I remember the first time we went midnight gardening. My father came upstairs to our bedrooms and shook each one of us awake. It was late. We were all fast asleep in our beds. He said, "Come on. We're going to play a fun game. We're going MIDNIGHT GARDENING!" HUH? What was that? He sounded so excited and happy! All six of us kids jumped out of our beds. Our parents were getting us up in the middle of the night to play a game? This was the BEST! We tripped over each other getting to the bottom of the stairs. Still in our jammies, we were jumping up and down wondering what this new game was. Ma had our shoes lined up, so we all scrambled into them, grabbed our jackets, and headed out the door. We loaded up into our old Volkswagen transport van and headed down the road. Our excitement was off the charts. We were GOING somewhere to play this game! In the middle of the night!

About ten minutes later we pulled off the main road onto a dirt path between two huge fields. This area was commonly known as "The Muck" where acres and acres of vegetables were grown. My parents jumped out of the front seats and opened the side door of the van. They stood there and explained the rules to us. First thing was you must be SILENT. As exciting as the game was, you could lose if you screamed, hollered, or giggled too loudly. Second item: everyone got his or her own pillowcase. Now for the fun part. We had to run into the big fields and fill our pillowcases with only the largest vegetables we could find. No little ones. Whoever had the most when we got home, won. How cool is THAT? Off we went like six horses in the Kentucky Derby. The oldest went to the left. The second went to the right. The rest of us scattered in between. I looked back and saw my father helping Tim, the youngest, fill his pillowcase. Tim was little, so we didn't mind.

I felt the soft dirt sink under my sneakers as I lifted leaves and vines and found the biggest veggies I could. I suppressed giggles and screams of delight when my treasures appeared. It didn't take long and all of us were piling back in the van with our pillowcases full of loot. Six kids, all hot, sweaty, laughing, and talking sibling smack. My father and mother were grinning and telling us what a great job we all did and asked if we had fun.

We whooped it up in the back of that van and were almost in tears. What a riot! What a fantastic game!

When we arrived home, my mother made us all wash our hands and feet because we were caked in "the muck" and she didn't want to be scrubbing mud from everything for the next week. Six pairs of hands and feet all cleaned and ready for bed. Upstairs we went, still ecstatic yet exhausted from the adventure we just had. We slept soundly for the rest of the night.

The next morning as we all sat around the kitchen table eating breakfast, our parents proudly exclaimed it was a six-way tie. We ALL won. Each of us had the exact same number of veggies in our pillowcases. Isn't that something? The six of us looked around the table and grinned. We were ALL winners. Then the folks got serious on us. They explained that midnight gardening was a fun game, but it was something else too. Everyone settled down. We knew when they were serious about a topic, and we had to pay attention. That was when my father explained that the owners of all those big fields get busy taking care of all that land. He went on to say it's a lot of work, even if you have helpers. And sometimes they just don't get to the fields in time to get the ripe vegetables and then what happens? They rot. They go to waste. And if you don't pick the biggest ones, then the smaller ones won't have room to grow, and they'll just rot too. My father's face looked sad. He told us we were actually helping the big muck farmers by clearing out the ripe vegetables that they couldn't get to in time. BUT . . . and this was the most important part . . . we couldn't tell anyone about it. We couldn't go anywhere and brag about how we, six little kids, helped the big muck companies. No. That could NOT happen. That's when my mother stepped in. She was usually the one to instill manners and integrity in us. "Virtue is its own reward," she said. Her expression had us befuddled.

I asked, "What does that mean?"

Ma went on to explain that whenever you do something nice for someone, do it quietly. If you brag about it or bring attention to it, that just cancels out all the goodness of your deed. If you have to say, "LOOK AT ME! LOOK AT HOW GREAT I AM!" then you're really not a very nice person at all. That's why we could never tell anyone about helping the muck farmers. Besides, we didn't want the muck farmers feeling bad that they couldn't get to their crops on time, right? That morning, at that big kitchen table, we all promised we would never tell anyone about our midnight gardening.

We "helped" the muck farmers a few more times that summer and fall. Each time was just as exciting as the first. Maybe even more so because we were now filled with pride knowing what a good thing we were doing.

It took many years for us to catch on that we were just extremely poor and stealing food to survive that summer. My parents knew this was wrong. They agonized over it. But this was almost a victimless crime in their eyes. What's worse? Taking a few pillowcases of food from acres and acres of land, or letting your children go hungry? I give them credit for their creative process and how they made a game of it for us. Looking back, I see it was wrong . . . but it was a blast.

My mother died in 2002. My father checked out in 2013. To even things up, I've carried donations of canned food in pillowcases to pantries over the years. Somewhere deep down, I can hear them laughing.

Fast forward to modern times. I still can't feel sorry for people who have to put the latest electronic gadgets on layaway for their young children. I can't muster up sympathy for their pre-teen children getting "only" a thousand-dollar iPhone. I'm not saying I wish every child could have it rough, but maybe, just maybe, they shouldn't have everything handed to them on a silver platter. Just a thought.

DANIELLE'S HOUSE

Anyone who has known me for any length of time can attest to my affinity for what I term "out there" topics in life. I'm not into chasing UFOs or tracking down Bigfoot, but if that's your thing, then do it. I'll be the first person to read your stories and check out your pictures because part of me really wants to believe strange things exist. I love a mystery. I love the unexplained and unexplainable. I think that's why I get phone calls or messages occasionally and receive invitations for visits. People experience unnerving events in their homes and want someone else to validate their feelings or suspicions. Again, I'm not on the prowl for anything. I don't plan to start my own ghost hunting series for television or a YouTube channel. I'm not an exorcist, but I do smudge homes and do my own special brand of juju. My motto: can't hurt; might help. I like going to check out a home or a building that other people deem worthy of a second opinion. One of these places was an old home owned by a lady named Danielle.

Danielle called and introduced herself. She said, "You don't know me, but I know about you." Uh-oh. My first thought was what did I do this time? I lead a low-key and boring life, so I wasn't really too concerned. I figured this lady wanted either reiki or some cupcakes. I serve up both. And then some.

"I hear you're into . . . uh . . . checking out . . . uh . . . places that are maybe . . . different?" Her verbal stumbling told me she wasn't used to talking about whatever strange things were happening to her. I've seen this so many times. People are afraid to be labeled as crazy, hysterical attention-seekers. Nobody wants to be known as the loony lady who imagines ghosts haunting her home. I totally understood her hesitation.

"Danielle, if you have a haunted house, barn, or workplace, then please tell me about it. I love this stuff." I tried to convey my enthusiasm for the unknown. I was hoping she'd open up to me. After all, she called, so let's get this ball rolling.

I could hear her take a deep breath. Then she said, "I live right in town. I'm told this is one of the older homes that has survived all these years. It's had a lot of updates, of course. I've only owned it for two months but . . ." her voice trailed off. I waited patiently. "But I don't know if I'm welcome here."

I understood immediately. If you're not used to certain "energies" in a place, they can cause you to be a bit edgy. Even if you can't put your finger on any particular incident, your body and spirit can sense something is off kilter and it'll affect you. I could tell she was dealing with something but didn't quite know how to explain it.

"This house is beautiful. It's big and roomy and everything I want and need. But I don't feel like I fit here. Am I crazy?" Danielle was flustered.

I explained to her she was NOT crazy. People and buildings have personalities, an energy about them. For some reason her house's vibe wasn't matching up with her own and that might be why she felt out of place. When I talk to people, many of them can tell me about homes they've entered and right away they felt welcomed and comfortable. Other times, they've gone somewhere and couldn't wait to leave. I think we all experience that to some extent.

"This is a lot to ask, but could you come over and visit for a while?" Danielle asked softly. "It's not just the anxious feeling. I've . . . had some . . . strange stuff going on here. At least I think I have. Maybe I've imagined it. Could you spend a night here with me?"

There was something in her voice that said she was holding out on me. She wasn't giving me the whole story. I checked my calendar and told her what night I could come stay with her. I accepted her invitation thinking I'd go meet her, maybe pick up on some odd energy in her home, and reassure her she's not crazy. Danielle's invitation turned out to be one of the more interesting "out there" experiences I'd had in quite some time.

I arrived at Danielle's house promptly at 7:30 p.m. on a Friday night. Her home sat on a double lot in town. The paved driveway led from the street to the back of the property where the old carriage house had been converted into a garage. I parked, stepped out of my car, and stood there looking at this beautiful three-story home. It must have been quite the landmark in its early days, as it was exquisite even after all these years. The fine woodwork and the attention to detail were magnificent. From the large bay windows to the intricate window frames, every nuance was a visual pleasure.

Danielle met me at the back door. I entered a tidy mudroom which led into a large kitchen. I immediately felt something but didn't say a word to Danielle. I didn't want to get her wound up or anxious. When I visit someone in a situation like this, I like to form my own opinions based on what I experience, not what they've told me. The house tour started in the kitchen. We then went through the dining room, living room, den, and a peek into the bathroom. We continued up to the second floor and toured the four bedrooms, a bathroom, and the little sitting area near the front hallway window. There was a narrow stairway leading up to the third floor where the attic had been converted into what I imagine was a playroom for children years ago. A blackboard was attached to one wall. There were several shelves low to the floor that may have held games or toys. Two built-in benches were against one wall, and they opened for storage inside. Quite a good use of space, I thought to myself. We went back downstairs to the kitchen where Danielle led me to another door. Her hand hesitantly reached for the doorknob, and she opened it slowly. Her face went a little white and she said, "Nothing down there but the washer and dryer."

I asked if I could go down to look around.

"Sure. Um . . . I'll put on some coffee while you check it out, okay?" She had a worried look on her face, so I told her coffee sounded good and I'd be right back.

It only took me about a minute to figure out why she was so hesitant to go down cellar. The energy down there was thick. I mean THICK. Nothing sinister, just truly palpable. I was almost to the bottom of the stairs, and I could feel the hair on my arms and the back of my neck standing up. I slowly walked around the basement. I didn't feel threatened or scared. Just aware. I knew someone was down there, but not in the literal sense. A strong scent of body odor lingered in the air. I looked around and saw the washer and dryer, but there were no dirty clothes sitting in a hamper or clothes basket. The place was spotless.

I went back up to the kitchen where the smell of fresh coffee was brewing. We'd already agreed to stay up as late as possible on Friday night, so the coffee would help keep us alert. I'd asked Danielle not to tell me any specifics about what she'd experienced in her home because I didn't want her to influence my senses or sway me in any direction. We chatted about her job, our families, movies, and music. Every so often during our conversation, I'd sense someone else moving about the kitchen. As we visited, my eyes were roving around the room, but I didn't see anyone, only sensed them. At times, Danielle would pause and look over my shoulder or to her left, and then continue talking. I knew. She knew.

We moved from the kitchen into the living room. We talked about the house's history, and she said she'd read the deed and abstract and recognized a few names of the previous owners. Their descendants still lived in the area. The house was built back in the early 1800's and was one of the nicer homes in town. It had always been a one-family home, never converted to apartments or a business. I'm always tickled when people can maintain old homes and not tear them up or subdivide them. They just lose character once they're dissected.

As we were talking in the living room, the same sense of other people being present was felt by both of us. More than once, Danielle caught my eye and I just nodded to her, acknowledging the company we both felt.

"Danielle, would you mind if I tried a couple of things? I'd like to see if anyone wants to make their presence known to us."

Danielle nodded and said, "Please, do whatever you want to do. If you can get anything to happen, then I'll know I'm not nuts. It's crazy, but I just need to know I'm not imagining everything."

I got up and walked to the kitchen where I'd set my duffel bags down on the floor. I picked up my smaller bag and took it into the living room. I knelt in front of the coffee table and set up two white candles. I lit them and waited to see if there was any draft that would make them flicker. I'm always looking for a reasonable explanation for any odd occurrences before I jump the gun and say "ghost!" Then I set up a small contraption that held a chain necklace with a ring that belonged to my mother on it. The chain dangled down about twelve inches from the top of the small structure with the ring at the bottom of the chain. I gave it a little tap to see if it could swing freely, and it did. I held my finger against the ring to stop it from swaying. I reached back into my bag and pulled out a pencil and a marble. Danielle's face had that "What the hell?" look and I chuckled lightly. I told her I like to give plenty of options to the spirits as means of contact. She smiled. I placed the marble and pencil on the coffee table not far from the candles. Then I took a seat on the couch.

I looked over at Danielle. "Are you ready? I can't promise anything, but it's worth a shot."

Danielle bit her lower lip and nodded at me. "Let's give it a whirl!"

I took a few deep breaths and quietly asked, "If there's anyone here with us tonight, we'd like to talk with you. Please make yourself known." And we waited.

Nothing happened. We waited about five minutes. The candles stayed the same, the ring on the chain didn't move. The pencil and marble remained still.

I asked again, "If anyone would like to make their presence

known, please do. We're ready to listen to you."

We waited. A couple of minutes after my second invitation, the marble rolled about three inches to the left. Not towards the edge of the table, but towards the ring and chain.

Danielle's eyes were getting big. She gawked at me as I put my fingers to my lips, signaling to keep quiet.

I started talking. "We see you're with us. We'd like to speak with you. Are you alright with Danielle living in this house?"

I watched the chain and ring. If the ring started swinging in a vertical direction, the answer would be yes. If it swung side to side, the answer would be no. I watched. I noticed Danielle was following my line of sight and was keeping an eye on the ring too. Sure enough, it started to move. Danielle's hands dug into the arms of the stuffed chair she was sitting in, but then remained perfectly still. The ring moved forward slightly, then back. It was rocking vertically. I smiled.

Looking over at Danielle, I softly said, "This is a good sign. They said yes. They're ok with you being here, meaning they aren't trying to chase you away."

The candle that was closer to Danielle flickered, almost went out, then flared back to life again. Danielle let out a little nervous giggle. Then the marble rolled another inch, but back toward its original position on the table.

"I'm not crazy! I'm not imagining all of it. Ask another question," Danielle whispered.

"Is there any way you will leave this house so Danielle can be alone?" I asked. It's always best to ask a spirit to leave the house instead of being rude and telling it to go away. Remember, it's their choice to stay or go, so unless you believe those Hollywood horror movies, it's really not up to you. Besides, you know what always happens in the last minute of those movies. Yeah. The chandelier starts rocking again, or a door opens slowly. The Boogeyman is still there, right?

We watched the ring. It swung side to side. Nope, the spirits aren't leaving.

"Are you happy staying in this house? Is that why you

won't leave?"

Forward motion. And back.

Danielle looked over at me nervously and asked, "So what does that mean? Are they saying they'll haunt this house forever? Will I always have them here?"

I shrugged and gave a palms-up gesture. "Looks that way. I don't think they're harmful. Seems to me you have some roommates. Or, more accurately, THEY have a roommate. They were here first. You're in their space, no matter what the deed says."

"Can I ask them something?" Danielle was feeling a little less nervous and a little more confident now.

I nodded and waved my hand towards the coffee table. "Ask away."

She nervously cleared her throat and quietly asked, "Will I be harmed in this house? Are you going to hurt me?"

Our eyes were glued to the chain and ring. It began swinging left to right, very strongly.

I looked at Danielle and could see her shoulders relaxing slightly. All this time she was worried about getting hurt. I felt bad for her. I understood how anyone would feel scared, intimidated, even freaked out by supernatural happenings in their homes, but to actually fear physical harm had to be horrible.

I asked Danielle if she'd ever felt threatened in any way in her house. She thought about it and answered no. She felt fear, but only because she didn't know what she was facing. She didn't know what the sounds, smells, or physical sensations were all about, so she was naturally afraid of them. I reassured her this was totally normal, but unless she absolutely, positively felt like she was in danger or if she'd experienced anything that could cause her bodily harm, then there was nothing to worry about.

We sat in the living room chatting for another couple of hours. The candles flickered at odd times and the marble moved slightly twice more. The pencil never moved. The ring and chain didn't move anymore. Danielle didn't go into detail, but she told me to expect more activity at night. This piqued my interest.

I blew out the candles, retrieved my overnight bag from the kitchen, and Danielle showed me to one of her guest rooms upstairs. We said good night and with a grin on her face, she tossed in, "Sweet dreams."

Sweet dreams. Was I dreaming? Or did I really feel that hand on the side of my face? Did I feel someone sitting on the edge of my bed, causing my body to lean toward it? Was that the same odor I smelled in the cellar? I remember waking up at 3:30 a.m. I pulled the covers off me and went down the hallway to the bathroom. When I returned to bed, the two pillows that were side by side at the head of my bed were stacked one on top of the other. I don't sleep with two pillows so I certainly wouldn't stack them on top of each other.

I moved one pillow off to the edge of the bed and climbed under the covers to go back to sleep. I must have been in and out of it for the next couple of hours because I couldn't tell what was real and what was happening in my dream-like state of mind.

I awoke a little before 6:00 a.m. and went downstairs. Danielle wasn't awake yet, so I tried to be as quiet as possible. I reached the living room and noticed the marble and pencil that had been left on the coffee table were now sitting next to my small duffel bag that I'd placed near the couch, where I'd been sitting. I sat down on the couch in a slow, controlled manner. I concentrated on the ring still hanging from the chain. I whispered, "Danielle gets a little freaked out by all the activity going on here. You don't have to go away, but can you be a little less active? Please?" I watched as the ring swung forward then back. I smiled. I never told Danielle about that request. I picked up my candles, marble, pencil, and the chain and ring. I put it all back in my bag and carried it out to the kitchen where I made coffee. I heard Danielle come downstairs a few minutes later.

"How'd you sleep?" she asked.

"Pretty good. And I think I had company," I told her.

We discussed the smell in my room, like the body odor

down cellar. I told her about feeling a hand on my face and the sensation of someone sitting on my bed. I laughed about the pillows being stacked. Danielle said she's experienced all of that and more. She went on to tell me about how the curtains are sometimes closed when she gets home from work, but she knows she opened them in the morning. Other times she'll find a spoon in the hallway. She sometimes hears whispers down cellar. Still, nothing that made her feel unsafe or like she needed to call the police.

Danielle told me my visit comforted her. She appreciated being validated, and knowing she wasn't losing her mind was priceless. I asked her if she felt she could live with roommates and she laughed. She said yes, now that she knows nothing bad will happen to her. It'd still be a little off-putting, she admitted, but that big old house was worth it.

I got dressed, packed up my bags, and headed home. I wished her good luck and to keep me posted on any new activity. She promised she'd keep me in the loop.

A few months later I received an email from Danielle. She'd done some digging into the history of her home and found her house had been used for the underground railroad. Her house was one at which slaves would stop and take shelter on their way into Canada. More research showed the original drawings for the house had a small room down cellar which was eventually filled in and a wall was placed over the small entryway.

She told me there hasn't been as much activity as before, but when something odd does happen, now she just says hello and carries on with her day.

Danielle also keeps a marble and a pencil on her coffee table. You know . . . just in case.

TURNERS

When my family moved up here to the outskirts of Brasher Falls in 1974, we had our work cut out for us. My folks bought an old, run-down farm that needed a lot of repairs and upgrades just to get it workable. My father humped it through long hours preparing the barn and milkhouse for dairy cows. My mother labored in the house trying to make it livable for all of us. Money was tight. Very tight. With no income yet, my parents had to make every penny they had count. Eventually the barn was up to snuff and cows were purchased, so milk was made. That meant a milk check would arrive once a month. Still, frugality was the name of the game as we were getting on our feet.

During that first year we met many of the neighbors and local fellow dairy farmers. One of those families was the Turners. The Turners owned and operated a small farm like ours, about ten miles away as the crow flies. Rick and Sharon were in their late 30's and had two young children, about 8 and 10 at that time. Rick was of average height but had a little bit of a paunch on him. Sharon was matronly already as if she'd given up before her clock had hit 40. The Turners were friendly folks, and whenever they'd stop by for a visit, everyone had a good time. The only thing that irked my parents was the fact that the Turners always seemed to stop in at suppertime. Having eight mouths to feed every night was hard enough on my mother's already stretched household budget. Adding in two extra adults and two more growing children, all with extremely hearty appetites, well, that put more of a strain on the food allowance than was appreciated. And yet, my mother was never one to turn anyone away from her table. She taught us it's rude to eat in front of others, and you should always offer your guests whatever you're eating.

At least twice each week the Turners dropped in at 7:00 in the evening. They knew Oscar was just finishing up with milking and would be coming in for supper. Oscar preferred to get the chores done and then sit down to his evening meal, and not the other way around. He always said working on a full stomach made him uncomfortable and I understand that. Besides, winding down with supper and then a little television was relaxing after a long day of farming.

One evening the Turners dined with us and after supper all of us kids went outside to play. Yes, that happened. It was common back in the olden days to go play outside. The adults stayed inside talking about milk prices, crops, equipment, and so on. While we were outside throwing a baseball around, Robbie Turner casually said, "Boy, your mom's a good cook!"

What a nice thing to say. I nodded and said, "Thanks. She's had a lot of practice with all of us!" meaning our own family of eight.

That's when he replied, "Yeah, we like to come here because your mom's a good cook and the food is free! Mom says she likes not having to cook or do dishes, so we just come here and eat free food." Out of the mouths of babes, right? My siblings and I looked at each other. Yup. We all heard the same thing.

After another hour or so, the Turners left. We went inside and told our parents about the "free food" conversation with Young Turner. That's when my folks knew they had to do something. They were NOT cheap or stingy people by any means, but when you're barely scraping by for your own family and then someone else who is better off financially comes along and mooches . . . well, that's not acceptable.

One night Mick said to Oscar, "Hey, let's try something different tonight." One eyebrow went up on Oscar's forehead. "NO, not like THAT!" she laughed and swatted his arm. "I'm guessing the Turners are due tonight or tomorrow, so would you mind grabbing a light snack before chores? Then when you come in for supper, we'll sit around the table and have coffee or play cards, but not have supper until AFTER they go?"

Oscar smiled. "That's a great idea. Okay, I'll have some toast before I head to the barn."

And sure enough, the Turners showed up, just like clockwork, at 7:00 p.m. Oscar came into the house, washed up, and casually grabbed a cup of coffee and sat in his sturdy wooden chair at the end of the table. The Turners were already seated with their coffee cups in front of them. The expectation of another free meal was written all over their greedy faces. All of us kids were in on Ma's plan and anxious to see how it would play out.

We took our places around the big table. The adults drank coffee, the kids had Kool-Aid. My mother reached over to the shelf near her chair and grabbed the deck of cards and started shuffling. "Let's play Hearts!" she happily suggested.

My father countered with, "Okay, but I'm feeling lucky tonight, so get ready to lose!" Everyone laughed. The Turners sat there with confusion written on their faces. They didn't dare ask about supper. We played cards for well over an hour with lots of laughing, smack-talking, and finger pointing.

When it was obvious there wasn't any free supper to be had, Rick looked at Sharon and said, "Damn, it's getting late. We'd better get going." Sharon nodded and stood up, collected their kids, and said good night to us.

When their tail lights were down the road, my parents looked at each other and burst out laughing. "FINALLY!" exclaimed my mother. She then opened the warm oven and pulled out meatloaf and the pan of mashed potatoes she'd made earlier. I grabbed a stack of plates and my brother counted out the forks and knives. We all dug into our supper with a little extra glee that night figuring we'd outsmarted the moochers.

Not. So. Fast.

Apparently, the Turners weren't discouraged enough to

take a hint. They must have thought that one evening was a fluke. Just when we resumed our usual 7:00 p.m. suppertime, they showed up again. I could see the look of defeat on my mother's face as she saw the Turner's station wagon pull into our driveway. Oscar was just as pissed. Before the Turners reached the back door, my father winked at her and said, "I've got this. Just play along." Then he looked at us kids and nodded and we knew something was up and to roll with it.

Again, we all sat down at the table. The soup was watered down a little bit now, and the baked potatoes were cut in half so there would be more portions of food for everyone, including our self-invited guests. Everyone ate and chatted like normal. My father was a fast eater, so he usually finished first. That night he seemed to be really wolfing his food. I guess that's normal of a hard-working farmer, right? When he was finished with his plate, he casually set it down on the floor next to his chair and that's when our St. Bernard ambled over to it. She licked the plate clean. Oscar monopolized the conversation at this point, so all eyes were on him. As he was talking about how well the corn was coming on the southwest field, he reached down and picked up the dog-licked plate. Then he stood up and slowly walked to the cupboard and placed the "clean" plate on the stack of other plates. My mother's eyes were bugging out of her head. She didn't say a word. None of us kids said a word. Oscar then sat back down and continued with his ideas on why the corn was growing so well.

The Turners saw everything. But said nothing.

After supper, our guests didn't stay very long. They really had to get going and off they went. As their car was backing out of our driveway, my mother sprinted to the cupboard and pulled the top plate and five plates under it out of the cupboard and placed them into the sink of hot, soapy water.

"Do you think that did it?" Oscar asked.

"We can only hope!" Mick replied.

They turned and looked at us. Giggles started. Giggles turned into laughs. Tears happened.

The next night we waited for our guests to arrive.

They didn't.

And they didn't show up the night after that. Or any night that week.

The Turners did show up the following week, but they popped in at about 4:00 p.m., well before evening chores. The adults hung out in the kitchen drinking coffee for about an hour.

The Turners never came for supper again, only coffee in the late afternoon.

Nothing was ever mentioned about their last supper with the King family.

LASER HAIR REMOVAL

The following was an email I sent to my brothers and sisters many years ago. 100% true story.

Dear Sibs,

As some of you know, I've recently started the process of laser hair removal on my lower legs, upper legs, and my bikini line. I've been reading about this for a while now and it's always appealed to me. Well, wouldn't you know it, Mary has had it done already! When I asked her about it, she said, "Oh, it stings a little bit, but it's not bad at all!" Folks, I have one thing to say about Mary . . . she lies. Sure, it's relatively painless. Sure, it only stings for a minute. In the following paragraphs I'll try to describe my first visit. As you all know, I'm not one prone to exaggeration or wild bouts of the imagination. What you are about to read is real and true.

About a month ago I saw an advertisement in the Sunday paper touting the wonderfully new and virtually painless hair removal system. I still remember my ninth-grade English teacher, Mrs. Delores Post, telling us that "virtually" meant "almost, but not quite." I called the number to get all the details on this virtually painless procedure and was connected with a lovely lady who read all the propaganda from her cue cards. It sounded pretty damned good to me! Expensive, to be sure. It'll run a total of about $2300 for both legs all the way from the ankle to the wazoo, the bikini line (you can determine how big or how small your bikini is), and the treatment of some veins. I don't have varicose veins, but I do have that interstate map thing going on behind my knees and on my lower thighs. If Brasher Falls is the BUTT of the world, and Miami is the HEEL, then somewhere right around the Carolinas I have some serious I-95 action happening. Anyway, when all was said and done, I looked at my schedule and we made an appointment for my first visit. The kind lady on the other end of the line had set the hook. That was the last painless moment in this episode.

I drove over to Potsdam to this really nifty building that houses several doctors. Most of them are spread-n-peek doctors who smile a lot. Hey, they work in a college town. Wouldn't YOU? I went in and introduced myself to the receptionist. Oh yes, she was the one who recruited me last week. Please fill out these ten forms saying you understand laser treatment is usually safe and usually harmless and your first born may have three eyes, but other than that you'll be happy (and you won't sue). I didn't even have to wait long, maybe 10 minutes, when a very nice-looking doctor came out and introduced himself to me. Hubba-hubba-hubba. Here's a cutie who's going to see my Sasquatch legs and my 1970's Richard Pryor 'fro down below. Groovy. They said to let the hair grow for about a week before treatment, so they'd know what they were working with. Hey, ask and ye shall receive.

The doc escorted me back to what I now refer to as the Fiery Office of Hell. It didn't LOOK bad. Didn't SMELL bad. Didn't even have any blood splattered on the walls or fingernail marks on the doors. How bad could this be? My confidence was high. Mere mortal that I am, I sat there like a kid waiting for my first gold star from my Kindergarten teacher. My handsome doctor went through all the paperwork again, just to make sure I understood everything. He casually mentioned there would be some mild discomfort. Hey, no problem. Mild discomfort? I can handle that. Hell, I've handled mild discomfort every month since I was a teen. What does he think I am? A city babe who's never had as much as a hangnail before? Jeepers! Gimme some credit here.

It was time to take off the jeans and socks and get down to

business. I dropped my knickers, tossed off my socks and stood there in white panties and t-shirt. They said to wear white panties because dark colors draw the laser and if you're covering up something you don't want zapped, you have to be careful. I believe the doc was impressed with my follicle gifted legs and bikini line. I could donate to the Hair Club for Men. He then asked where I'd like to start. Seeing how this was my first venture into the laser field, I told him to start wherever he thought best. He went right for the bikini line (typical man). He said that place was usually the most sensitive and we should get that out of the way first. He's the expert, not me, so I smiled and nodded. Now I know why they do that part first. Because "sensitive" is a nice way to say it stings, burns, and hurts like hell. I don't know about the rest of you, but I was blessed with LOTS of double hair shafts in my bikini line. I have many sets of twins down there. Double my pleasure, double HIS fun. So, the doc put me in the stirrups, just like an annual spread-n-peek exam. He and his nurse pulled out a couple of tubes of Kentucky Jelly, also known as KY, and started smearing about two and half pounds on the left side of my Enchanted Forest. He then turned to his left and fiddled with a few dials on this machine that looked oddly enough like a welding machine where I work. Hmmmm. First bit of fear strikes me. Then he takes an interesting gadget about the size of a cordless screwdriver, with what looks like a one inch sewing machine foot on the end of it, to my groin. I figure hey, how bad can it be? He's lubed me up like we're gonna make a movie for PeeWee Herman's enjoyment and it's only a little itty-bitty laser. ZAP! OW! He moved the little zinger an inch or so down my hairline. ZAP! OW! ZAP! OW! ZAP! OW! He was working in a southward direction, and I had my doubts if he'd make it to the Mason-Dixon Line before I squashed his head between my knees. But I bore with it. It felt like he was lighting wooden matches, blowing them out and quickly touching them to my delicate skin. The doc informed me that dark hair really draws the laser beam and HOLDS the heat. No kidding? So that's what I'm feeling? HEAT? I thought he was taking a flippin' flame thrower and leaning into me down there. I thought he'd turned into Arnold Schwarzenegger on a really bad day. But I held on. ZAP! OW! ZAP! OW! On and on and on this went. I had to thank my lucky stars I'm only French and not Armenian. He made his way down to my lower Wazoo-land area and asked me just how far I wanted to take it. Well, hell. I already felt like I'd slid down a sandpaper banister without undies, so keep going, doc. I pulled my panties over just a little bit on either side, and he inched ever-so-close to the gates of heaven. Next time I go, remind me to put some Chapstick on down there. I was lying there in the most prone (or so I thought) position and he was down there ZAPPING my zippity-do-das until they were burning. That's another part that Mary forgot to tell me . . . you SMELL the burning hair. Yes, YOUR burning bush. I almost got religious at that point, but I didn't think Moses would come save me, so I extinguished that thought (pun intended). When all was said and done, I was hot, hot, hot and red, red, red on my OH-ZONE layer. They set a couple of ice packs on my groin and man, did that feel good. I even thanked them for it. They gave each other that knowing look. (Ha-ha! We burn her and she thanks us for giving her cold packs!)

If you think you just lie there and take the zapping, you're wrong. My doc had me flip over onto my side, one leg up in the air, balanced on his nurse's hip, ass up in the air like a cat in heat, legs splayed this way and that. I felt like I was auditioning for Hustler's Beaver Hunt. All I could think of was, "Where's the fat greasy guy with the Polaroid?" Dignity is thrown out the window when you get this kind of hair removal.

Then it was time to move on to my legs. He said he'd do the upper legs first and hey, I won't feel as much MINOR DISCOMFORT as in my bikini area. Oh gee, that's too bad. I really wanted to get my money's worth. Can ya pour some kerosene on first? Nope. He just squeezed out enough KY jelly onto my upper thigh to make it look like a school of jellyfish was having an orgy on me. Then he continued. ZAP! ZAP! ZAP! Hey! He was right. This wasn't bad at ALL. I was getting pretty happy about it. I could barely feel a little bit of tingling. Until . . . he got to my KNEE. I was learning the ins and outs of this laser stuff. If you have some meat where you're getting zapped, then it's not bad. If you're in a thin area, or an area close to the BONE, then it's going to hurt like hell. Again. I have knobby knees and they're hairy. ZAP! OW! ZAP! OW! It felt like I had knees the size of Oprah's ass by the time he was done zapping me. Then he worked his way down to the bottom of my leg. Again, not bad. Until he hit the friggin' ankle. Bones? You betcha. Hairy? OH, yes. The worst part of this whole thing was the doc was smiling. The bastard. I only wish I'd had beans for breakfast. He zapped the ankles as if he was doing the Daytona 500 in slow motion. ZAP! move an inch ZAP! move an inch. He was enjoying this way too much.

This whole procedure was completed on one leg, then the other. It was the only time in my life I was downright grateful to not be a supermodel. If I'd had legs any longer, I would have had to leave them there and come back for them next week.

Then the doc asked me to flip over. He was going to zap the veins on the back of my legs. He says this would feel a little different. Um . . . different? In what way, I wondered. Like poking yourself in the eye with a sharp stick is a little different from slicing off your toe with a new shovel different? He fiddled with the knobs on his welder and adjusted it to the "James Bond" setting. You all know that movie where 007 nearly gets his nuts roasted? Well, this is about the same feeling, only instead of Goldfinger with Odd Job, I have Dr. Lastra with his nurse. Funny thing is she was approximately the same size as Odd Job . . . but much nicer. She gave me ice packs, remember? There I was, on my belly, which was hard to do considering I was as greasy as a used car salesman from my navel to my toes. How many of you know what KY jelly turns to when it's been exposed to air for over two hours? Something like sticky snot. Tacky. Gummy. I was feeling like someone had covered me in magazine glue boogers. And lying on paper on the table did NOT help the situation. That made it nearly impossible yet highly entertaining to turn over. But I digress. Lying on my belly, chunks of KY up and down my lower half, the doc started ZAPPING my veins. What he failed to tell me was "different" means "You'll feel ten very angry bumble bees fighting on the back of your knee." Why don't they say what they mean? He only had a few veins to do, so that didn't take long at all. Only what seemed like the amount of time it takes for a train to go by while you're sitting at the railroad crossing with a full bladder.

Finally, he was done. ALL DONE. Only 2 1/2 hours and mission accomplished. He said I did great but seeing how I'm so blessed with such dark hair and really "feel the burn," then we should probably break my next session up into two visits. He suggested I do the bikini line and upper legs in one visit and the lower legs and veins the next week. Golly, I really wanted to repeat this great experience, but again, he's the expert. I tried not to look like I'd just been dragged through Dante's Inferno while I smiled and agreed that splitting the visits up would be doable for me. He said I could get dressed and he left the room.

I looked down at myself. My legs and groin area were a nice hot pink. Well, what I could see through the shreds of table paper and gobs of KY that were drying more and more with every second that went by. I was beginning to look like a six-year-old's papier mâché project. I tried to wipe some of the gunk off me, but no way. I thought what the hell and reached for my jeans. How many of you have been swimming and have tried to yank your clothes on over a damp body? Same thing here, only with chunks of dried snot and scraps of paper clinging to my legs. Fortunately, my guardian angel was with me that morning and I had worn my looser jeans that day. This helped immensely. I rolled them onto my body like a denim condom. I walked out to the reception area to make my next appointments and all I could think of was John Wayne must have had this done before every movie. Now I know why he walked the way he walked. Wa-ha, little lady. I slid out to my car and actually started to breathe again. The crisp, fresh air with the lack of burning hair smelled good. I was supposed to go to kickboxing class that night, but

I decided to skip it. The doc said no strenuous exercise for two days after a treatment. Hell, patting my lips with Charmin was about as strenuous as I could manage for a few days.

All in all, I'd say it was quite an experience. My next appointment is in a week. Yes, I am continuing this treatment because: a. I've already paid in full for it. b. I am not a quitter. c. I really, really HATE shaving. d. I know there's an end to this. Only four to six treatments required with minor touch-ups in the future.

Well, that's pretty much it for my fun times here in Northern New York. If any of you are thinking of doing this treatment, I whole-heartedly say GO FOR IT!

Love,
Pendra

2022 update: just for the record, it took a few more sessions than the doc had originally estimated. It took me a total of twelve visits to kill the hair growth on my legs and bikini line. After my last session, the doctor looked at me and said he'd never worked on someone with such stubborn hair as mine. Remember, that was back in 2006 when these lasers were relatively new to the market. I believe the guy lost money on me, but hey, a deal's a deal. I signed a contract and he honored it. It's now 2022 and to this day I'm glad I had it done. Once in a blue moon I'll have an errant hair pop up here and there, but they're always very fine and soft, not boar hog bristles.

BONES

Sometimes things happen to us that we don't understand at the time but later in life, the meaning becomes clear. Other times an event will happen, and we never get an explanation why. Many years ago, I had an experience that, to this day, I can't explain. I can't rationalize. I can't decipher. Some of it is becoming clearer to me, but I still need to work on it.

I really enjoy traveling. I finally had a good job that paid very well so I could afford to hit the road. Or air. One of my favorite trips was to go south for a week or two during the harshest of the winter months up here in the North Country. This particular trip south was a cruise to several islands, including Jamaica. I was on a warm, sunny cruise leaving the coast of Florida for a week. It felt great to thaw out and miss the snow and ice back home. The ship made several stops along the way, and I did the typical touristy jaunts at every port. This one port in Jamaica is still etched in my memory.

I disembarked with my small backpack, carrying a big bottle of water, some snacks, my camera, passport, and money. I'm always careful about how I pack my valuables when I go on these excursions because I know there are pickpockets, swindlers, and, let's face it, some not so nice people out there just waiting for the rich Americans to get off the boat. I double checked everything and off I went. As I walked around the tiny village, I was approached by several entrepreneurs wishing to sell me some of their special "herb" or "mints" that would make me happy. I was happy enough, so I said no thanks, and politely moved away from them. As I wandered the narrow streets, I noticed a few vendors selling trinkets: jewelry, knick-knacks, t-shirts, and such. I didn't need any baubles, so I just kept moseying my way along the sidewalks. About an hour into my jaunt, I noticed a woman who looked about fifty years old. Kind of hard to tell with some people. She could have been a worn out forty. Didn't matter. What I did notice was she seemed to be watching me. She popped up at almost every little shop or stand that I paused at, and this was starting to annoy me. I brought my backpack around to the front of me and I carried it in a hug with both arms. I figured that would discourage any ideas she may have had of lightening my load.

I was wrong about this lady. She wasn't about to rip me off. Quite the opposite. She finally caught my eye, smiled, and walked up to me. She was short, no more than five feet tall and somewhat stout. Her hair was covered with a red scarf wrapped around her head several times. The dress she wore was a faded green and blue cotton shift that had seen its better days. But what I really noticed was her eyes. One was bright and clear, dark brown, but the white part of that eye was almost shining. Her other eye was a foggy grayish brown with an almost yellow cast to what should have been white. That eye looked like it belonged in a ninety-year-old woman. She smiled gently at me and in her Jamaican lilt said, "Yo modda. She wanna me to talk to yo."

Huh? I was polite and asked her to repeat herself. I apologized and said I didn't understand.

She repeated, "Yo modda. Yo momma." Oh, okay. My mother. Ha. My mother wasn't with me. My mother has been dead for a while. I smiled politely and nodded as I tried to inch away. She moved towards me, but for some reason I didn't feel threatened. She repeated herself, "Yo modda. She tell me she wanna talk to yo. Come sit wit me."

All right, I know how these con artists work. They take a chance that your mom, dad, grandparents, etc. are dead and they want to contact you. This woman was calm and not pushy. I had plenty of time on my hands, so I thought, why not? If anything,

I'll get a funny story out of it, right?

We walked back from the direction I started in, and she led me to a small booth where a gal I'm assuming was her daughter was selling scarves and jewelry. The younger woman nodded at me as I walked past her and sat down at a small table with the older woman. "Ma name is Ora. You da youngest girl of da parents, yes?"

I said, "yes, I am the youngest girl in my family." Good guess on her part, I thought. Again, a fifty-fifty chance of being right. Ora smiled at me and said, "Yo modda, she say you have good job, make lotta money for youself."

I nodded and said I did okay, but I wasn't rich by any means. I'm thinking, an American tourist on a cruise, so of course I have money. No brainer. She wasn't impressing me at all, but I was curious to see what other gems of wisdom she would come up with for me. "Yo modda say you scare her when you a itty bitty girl and yo got a big ol' cut on yo belly. Big cut. Yo bleed and bleed and bleed and she canna help yo 'cause she not walk right."

This is about the time I started silently freaking out. When I was four years old, I was in a water fight with my siblings one rainy afternoon. I was using a glass peanut butter jar to catch the rainwater from the eaves and splashing my siblings with it. I slipped on the wet grass and the jar went out of my hands, smashed on a flat rock in the yard, and I landed on the glass. I cut my belly open just below my ribs on my left side. I ran into the house screaming because every time my heart would beat, blood would pump out all over my belly and shorts. My mother was on crutches at the time due to an infected ingrown toenail. Fortunately, my father was home, so she hollered for him, and he scooped me up and took me to the emergency room to get stitched up. Thirty stitches inside and out. Okay, she had my attention now. And she knew it by how white I'd gone.

"Yo know I say da trute?" Ora was looking at me with an intense stare. I nodded slowly. I asked her to go on. I wondered what else my mother wanted me to know.

At that moment, Ora reached to her right and pulled a small cloth sack off a shelf. She opened the sack and asked me to hold my hands out. She made a cupping motion with her hands, so I cupped both hands and she dumped out a bunch of small bones. I almost dropped them because honestly, it grossed me out to have bones laid in my hands. I had no idea whose bones they were. Her soft fingers quickly reached under mine and supported my cupped hands. "Yo hode da bones for some minutes." I sat there staring at this pile of small bones in the palms of my hands. They were tiny. Dry. No meat or nasty stuff clinging to them. I asked what bones they were, and she replied chicken. WHEW! Okay, I could handle that. They looked too small to be human bones, so I could stop spazzing out now.

"Now yo close da hands an' you shake da bones." Ora cupped her empty hands and motioned a shaking movement like we were going to play Yahtzee. As I was shaking, she pulled out a cloth with several odd designs on it. On one corner there was a crudely drawn and painted moon. On another corner, a sun. There were what I interpreted as male and female bodies. Some cups, plates, boxes, and other small pictures roughly drawn and painted on this cloth laid before me. "Yo drop da bones now!" she instructed. She made the movement of opening her hands and scattering the imaginary contents onto the material, so I did too. The handful of chicken bones went this way and that. The bones landed all over the weirdly painted cloth below my opened hands.

Ora studied the bones and nodded softly. "Ahhh . . . ." And then, "Ohh, hmmm . . . ." I was about to speak but she raised her hand to me, palm first, without even looking at my face. I realized she was concentrating and would have a lot to say. I waited. My heart was beating pretty hard in my chest and my mouth was as dry as the desert. Even though I was on the lookout for a scam, I wanted to believe she had something more to tell me. Some tidbits of wisdom from my mother or any other family member who has died would have been a treat.

"Yo have da sadness in yo heart. Yo lose a brudder in bad

way." I looked at her cloudy eye and there was a tear forming. I told her yes, I did lose a brother. He was hit by a drunk driver many years ago. She lowered her head and studied the bones some more.

"Modda not got good wind. Hard to get air. But in her heart and in her head, dat's what took her." Staying calm, I told her yes. My mother had serious breathing issues, COPD, and she did pass from a stroke. More bone studying.

"Yo will have more of da sadness. I sorry for you, baby. Yo Papa go. He too sick to stay." I realized this was inevitable, seeing how my father was diagnosed with Parkinson's and Alzheimer's and everyone knew it was a matter of time. The fact that she knew my mother and one of my brothers were gone but my father wasn't, shook me.

"Sad, sad. Yo to be da baby of da family." I told her no, I'm not the baby of the family. I'm the youngest girl, but not the baby of the family. I didn't want to give anything away, so I sort of implied there may be several younger brothers, when, there was only one younger brother, and HE was the baby of the family.

Ora looked at me with the sincerest look and almost an apology on her lips.

"No, baby. YO be da baby of da family soon. Da brodda, he not good. He like yo modda. He sick in his heart." She tapped her breastbone to emphasize what was wrong.

By now I'm thinking I want to leave. She's hitting way too close to home. My younger brother was overweight, smoked, and didn't eat right. He worked long hours and didn't have time to take good care of himself. I worried about him, but he was a grown man who could make his own decisions. I didn't want this strange lady to tell me another one of my siblings was going to die, especially a younger sibling. I almost stood up to leave, but something held me there.

I gave a half-chuckle as if to laugh off her seriousness and decided to change the subject. I asked her if she could see my future. I asked about any good stuff happening because surely, I've had enough bad stuff, right? She could tell I was a bit unnerved and wanted to change course.

She glanced down at the bones again. "Ah. Yo love deep. Yo give yo heart too fast. Yo work so so hard at love but yo should not. Never work harder dan de man do. Da man should earn yo love." Then she went on to give me some details which I embarrassingly admit were true then and are true today. I fall too quickly. I give too much. I put my needs on the back burner every time. I never thought about this part of my visit with Ora until after a couple of future relationships were over. She was spot on with all her details of my time spent with two guys in particular. She nailed them. At the time, nothing made sense because nothing had happened yet. It wasn't until years later that her words rang true. I should have listened to her more closely and heeded her advice. But I didn't, and I paid for it.

I was sufficiently mind-warped and wanted to walk away, so I reached in my pocket and asked her how much I owed her for the reading. Her head tilted to the left and she said, "Nottin, baby girl." I laughed because I know they always take money. I asked again, this time sliding a ten-dollar bill across the table. She pushed it back and said no, she was just being the messenger for my mother, so she couldn't take my money. I got up to leave and she lifted the drawn/painted cloth by the corners and tied the bones up into a little pocket. She handed me the package and said, "Yo modda say she know yo will learn to read da bones someday. She want yo to have da bones. Yo study. Yo work da bones an dey talk to yo someday." I nodded, reached out, and she gently placed the wrapped bones in my hand. She smiled and patted my hand as I thanked her and said good-bye.

Fast forward many years later and here I am. I've never told anyone about this freaky moment on my vacation. I know how some people get weirded out by unexplainable events. I realize others think anything out of the ordinary is considered devil worship, cult activities, or whatever undesirable label you can slap on it. I can tell you this much, though, my mother was very much into ESP, life after death, communicating with the spirits, and so on. She used to read tarot cards, regular cards, and her own special deck of cards. She held séances, loved exploring haunted houses, and always wondered about the afterlife. Did she really come through to me via Ora? Kind of makes you scratch your head and wonder, doesn't it?

My little brother Tim died from a heart attack almost four years ago. Now I really am the baby of the family.

And to answer your question, yes. Yes, I still have that old cloth and the chicken bones. Occasionally I'll pull them out and shake the bones. I concentrate on what I see on the cloth, but it's not all clear to me just yet. Sometimes I think I have things figured out. Other times I'm grasping in the dark. I guess I'll just keep working on it and see what happens.

FIND YOUR STATUE

Sitting on a bench at the mall in Plattsburgh, I pulled out my list of items I was hoping to find. I'm not much of a shopper, so when I do make the trip, I like to get everything I need. I was ticking off the items I'd picked up already, circling the ones I still needed to find, and crossing out what was unnecessary and a waste of money. That's how my mind works.

An elderly gentleman sat down on the other end of the bench. He looked to be about seventy-five or so. The top of his head was bald and shiny. The wisps of remaining hair were gray and cut short. He wore wire-framed glasses perched on his abundant nose. The man's shirt was a starched white button-down and he wore a bolero tie which added a touch of character to his attire. His slacks were brown and neatly pressed with creases down the front of both legs. His feet were tucked into dark brown leather loafers. A hint of argyle socks escaped from below his trouser hem. I pegged him for about five-foot-seven and of average weight. Yet, when he sat down, his posture was perfect, and he suddenly looked much taller. I liked him already.

I wasn't staring by any means. I've become adept at the casual glance that takes a lot in at once. I enjoy people-watching and that probably comes from my days as a store dick when I was busting shoplifters at Jamesway. (Yes, I'm THAT old!) As this gentleman looked around, he finally turned his head in my direction and said, "Great day for a trip to the mall, huh?"

I turned to him, smiled, and gave a little bit of a shoulder shrug. "I'm not much of a shopper, so I guess this is a necessary evil." Everyone knows I'll talk to just about anyone.

He nodded, smiled, and I saw what must have been perfect dentures because nobody that old has all their own teeth, right? Didn't matter because they looked good on him, and only added to his pulled-together demeanor. This man has had a pretty good life. It was easy to see that he obviously had money, had his health, and probably some advantages a lot of people never get.

He introduced himself as Carl. Seventy-eight years young and getting younger by the day, according to him. We chatted for quite some time as shoppers milled about us. I felt as if I'd known him forever, as if I had grown up next door to him. We agreed about cell phones, the internet, and online banking. We admitted not everything has to go so fast or be so easy. Even though I was a bit younger than Carl, I seemed to fit into his way of thinking. I've been accused of being an old soul and I won't argue. I finally asked him what he did for a living. I was expecting him to say he had been a banker, maybe a doctor, or possibly a high-end lawyer.

He looked at me and asked, "How much time do you have?"

Ohhh . . . I knew this was going to be another opportunity to learn something. I've said it before, and I'll say it again, old people are a treasure trove of wisdom and knowledge.

"I'm on my day off. I have all the time in the world."

"I was homeless," he whispered.

Carl's eyes were what would be described as "rheumy." They were tired, yet also wise. "I was homeless and had nobody. It wasn't my fault, that's just the way things happened."

I gave a slight nod as if to say, "Please, go on." This was his story:

"I was homeless. I was living in Philly at the time. I'm an only child. Both of my parents were killed in a car accident right after I turned eighteen and had graduated from high school. I didn't have any relatives nearby to take me in. I didn't have any money to pay the mortgage. So, there I was, eighteen, and kicked out of the only home I knew because my parents were gone." The sadness was still fresh. It was written all over his face. Then he lifted his chin slightly and continued. "It was hard at first, living in a big city and not knowing what to do or where to go. A couple of friends let me stay a night here and a night there at their places, but nobody likes a bum taking up space. I had planned to go to college after high school, but . . . " and his voice trailed off. "Life hands you a rock. You just have to chisel away at it to find your statue."

I thought about that for a minute. He was right. We're all handed a life and what we make out of it is totally up to us.

Carl resumed his story. "It was really cold one day and I needed to get inside someplace warm, so I walked into a five-and-dime store on Penn Avenue. It wasn't a huge store, but big enough that I could wander around as if I was shopping and wouldn't draw any attention. Plenty of people were in there so nobody would notice me. At least I thought nobody would notice me, but that wasn't the case. The owner must have been watching me. I was so cold, so hungry, and so afraid he'd kick me out, but what he did was he saved my life. I'm not exaggerating. One man's kindness on a cold November day was the make-or-break moment for me. The owner was a big Italian man, Mr. Fornelli. He slowly walked up to me when nobody was near and asked if he could help me find something. I hung my head, knowing I didn't have any money to pay even if I did want something. I figured he was watching to make sure I wouldn't steal anything. I shook my head and then looked up at him. He must have seen how desperate I was. His eyes read mine and he put a hand on my shoulder. He told me he'd just made a batch of soup and if I had the time, would I try it out for him and let him know if it tastes all right."

My throat started feeling lumpy. Kindness always gets to me. I waited for Carl to go on.

"The owner of the store walked me to his lunch counter and asked me to take a seat on one of the red vinyl stools. He placed a large bowl of thick beef and macaroni soup in front of me. He put two large buttermilk rolls and some butter on a plate next to the bowl of soup. I wrapped my hands around the bowl to feel that wonderful heat. It was beautiful. I started eating the soup and rolls. Trying not to cry, I looked up at Mr. Fornelli and told him his soup was absolutely delicious and it needed nothing. The big man nodded and told me to take my time. I ate as slowly as I could, even though I was so hungry. I didn't want to finish too soon and have to leave the warmth of his store, so I stalled as much as possible. Finally, I knew I had to go. I knew I was being greedy and taking advantage of this man's generosity, but oh how I appreciated it. I put my spoon down in the empty bowl and looked for Mr. Fornelli to thank him. He was just coming around the end of the lunch counter and saw me standing there, awkwardly. He walked over and told me not to leave yet. He walked back to the burner where the soup had been simmering and ladled some into a to-go container. He placed several rolls and a spoon in the bag with the soup, walked over and handed it to me. I admit I was kind of choked up, but I managed to hold out my right hand and shake his as I squeaked out a thank you."

My eyes started misting up as Carl kept talking.

"I left that day feeling better about everything. Mr. Fornelli not only gave me two meals, but he gave me hope. Something in his attitude toward me made me feel like everything was going to be alright. I went back to Mr. Fornelli's store early the next morning. I arrived before he opened up because I didn't want him to see me there. I picked up the litter that was accumulating in front of his store and threw it into the big trash can on the corner of the street. I took some discarded newspapers and used them to wipe down the front windows that had dirt and cobwebs on them. It's hard to keep a place clean in the city. I went back there every day for a week, really early, to clean in front of Mr. Fornelli's store. I figured I owed him that much. One day he came out of the store as I was wiping his windows with crumpled newspapers. He told me the owner of the coffee shop across the street had called and told him a bum was hanging around the store every morning, so he thought he'd see what was going on. Mr. Fornelli laughed when he saw it was me and invited me inside. He took me to the lunch counter again and he made us both breakfast. I'm not talking about just toast and coffee. No. He made pancakes, eggs, home fries, and hash. He gave me juice and coffee. He kept saying eat up! Eat up! Finally, he asked what I was doing out front every morning. I told him I appreciated his kindness the week before. I said I knew he could have kicked me out of his store, but instead he let me warm up and he fed me. Mr. Fornelli hadn't expected anything in return for the meals. But he did notice how clean the sidewalk was and how good the windows looked for the past few days. That's when he said he didn't really have any job openings, but maybe we could work something out. I sat there and cried. Seriously, there I was, a grown man of eighteen, yet crying like a little kid. I started working for Mr. Fornelli that day. He said he'd pay me a little bit of cash and two meals a day if that was all right with me. I felt as if I'd just won the lottery."

I wanted to go hug Mr. Fornelli myself, but figured I was too late. Carl wasn't done yet.

"What I didn't know was Mr. Fornelli lived above the store he owned. He had a small apartment with his wife and two young kids. He and his wife cleared out a spot in the corner of the storage room at the back of the store. They put up a couple of curtains to make it a bedroom for me. They let me use the shower in their apartment and once a week I used their washer and dryer to clean my clothes. I worked every day at that store for Mr. Fornelli. Eventually I had enough money that I could get my own efficiency apartment. I was happy and grateful. I ran the store for him when Mrs. Fornelli died. I watched it for him on the days he had to take his kids to college or move them into their own homes. Eventually, Mr. Fornelli wanted to retire. He'd worked hard all his life, so he was planning on selling the store. Neither of his kids wanted to come back to Philly and take over for him. He offered it to me. We settled on a fair price and the rest is history."

He went on to tell me how he had met Anna and they had a

son, Jimmy. Anna had passed from breast cancer years ago. Their son Jimmy had been in the Air Force and was stationed in Plattsburgh. He showed sadness for the loss of his wife, and pride for his son. His son had settled in the Plattsburgh area when his hitch in the service was over.

"I worked that store until I couldn't work it anymore. I sold it. Yessiree, I sold it. One day a young man came in looking like a mutt who'd been kicked too many times. Something inside me said to take a chance on him. I swear I heard Mr. Fornelli's voice telling me to hire him, so . . . I hired him. Turned out he's a great worker. He has a real knack for retail. And his parents were so happy to see him working, saw how happy he was at the store, that they backed him financially. I keep tabs on him and he's doing pretty well. He's even added fancy coffees at the lunch counter. I sold the store to him and came up here to live with Jimmy and his wife. They have a guest suite off the side of their house. I have my privacy, but I also have Jimmy, Kathy, and the kids close by if I need them."

Carl was dealt a bad hand at an early age, but he didn't let it define him. He didn't let it defeat him. I'm in awe of his work ethic and strength. I'm grateful for Mr. Fornelli who saw the potential in Carl and changed his life for the better. I love how Carl then carried on Mr. Fornelli's generosity and kindness by hiring Victor, who is now the proud owner of that same store in Philly. I'm keeping my fingers crossed that if and when someone who is down and out goes into Vic's store looking for a job, that Vic passes this gift on to the next deserving person.

Life hands you a rock. You just have to chisel away at it to find your statue.

BRAZILIAN

WARNING: The following story contains descriptions of my girly bits, so if you're easily offended by a candid account of another one of my Lucy Ricardo episodes, please turn the page now. Thank you.

Lately, for the past 6 months or so, I've been reading all about how wonderful this "Brazilian wax job" is supposed to be. It's supposed to make your lower unit super smooth, soft, and ever so appealing to your lover. Several beauty salons in town offer this service. These are the same ladies who grind the calluses off your elephant feet and trim your talon-like toenails, so a Brazilian is just one more beauty job for them. For those of you who aren't familiar with what a Brazilian wax job is, please let me enlighten you.

You go into a quiet, private room and the lady in charge has you strip your pants and undies off and lie face-down on the table. She then carefully spreads your butt cheeks and, using a wooden tongue depressor, slathers very warm melted wax up and down your personal Grand Canyon. Once you're sufficiently covered in lava, I mean wax, she lays several small pieces of material on it. She presses gently so it'll adhere to the wax. After a few minutes when it's had a chance to cool slightly, she picks at the edge of the material and RIPS IT OFF! Several quick, smooth yanks and she's just rid you of all that hair where the sun doesn't shine. SMOOTH! SOFT! PAINFUL! I think these ladies secretly see how far up off the table they can get their clients to levitate. Once you're done with the back door, you can flip over and have her wax-and-rip the front. It's totally up to you on how you want it, or maybe it just goes on pain tolerance. You want just the bikini line done? No problem! You want only a "Little Hitler" left in the middle? Done deal. You're paying for it, so get as much or as little as you want. These gals aim to please. No skin off their . . . well . . . you know.

Mind you, I've never actually HAD this done to me. I've only spoken to a few gals who get this done on a regular basis, and to one lady who does this procedure. I may be mistaken, but I swear I saw a bit of a glint of glee in her eyes as she was describing the process.

At that time in my life, I was in what I like to call a "learning experience" with a guy I'll call Mitch. (I've changed from the words "relationship" or "mistake" to "learning experience" to be kinder to myself.) Mitch was French and had plenty of body hair for the both of us, so I thought I should look into (pun intended) these Brazilian wax jobs. The more I talked to these ladies, the more scared I became. I have a very low threshold for pain. I'm not into that whole "Beauty is Pain" line of thinking. But, yeah, being half French myself, and having already gone through the laser hair removal for my legs and bikini line, how bad could this be?

In the end (again, pun intended), I opted to NOT visit a salon. It really wasn't so much the pain part, it was the more intimate, personal part of this activity that bothered me. I was much younger than I am today, and a little bit shy about showing my girly bits to a total stranger or a friend. Hell, even my annual spread-n-peek appointment with my "Grin-o-cologist" is an uncomfortable time for me, but necessary, so I reluctantly do that every year. So, what were my options? Either stay fuzz-butted, or do it myself. I knew hot wax in my hands was just a disaster waiting to happen, so I opted for something else.

Nair! Nair is good for getting rid of unwanted hair and you can apply it yourself in the privacy of your own home. It doesn't involve strangers ripping off your heinie hairs for a fee.

Why not? I hit Walmart that afternoon and picked up a bottle of "sensitive skin" Nair. Liars. But I digress. Okay, my apologies to the Nair people. It wasn't their fault; it was my own.

As you know, I have been blessed with extremely healthy hair follicles. If you don't believe me, I can give you the name of my laser zapper guy in Canton. He said I was the most follicle-gifted woman he'd ever seen. See what happens when your mother mates with Sasquatch? Anyway, I figured I could do a "Brazilian" myself but without the pain and embarrassment. Note: I had NOT been drinking at that time.

I came home and headed straight to the bathroom. The Nair bottle said it could remove hair in "as little as three minutes." Okay, sure. Right. That must be for those blonde California chickies who have never had to grow hair in the winter. It takes at least five minutes to take off my mustache, so I knew I'd have to adjust the timing for my southern hemisphere. I stepped out of my britches and undies. I pumped a generous puddle of Nair onto my fingertips and slathered between my southside pillows. This was probably going to take at least ten, maybe fifteen minutes to work. Well, being the multi-tasker I am, I logged onto my email to see what's up while I was creating my intimate back door forest fire. Unfortunately, I opened an email from a friend who was having some serious love life issues. I read his email in which he poured his heart out about his girlfriend and asked what he should do about his latest boneheaded move. I'd been his personal "Dear Abby" for a long time. Of course, I was thinking deeply and pondering my every word to him as I typed out my female point of view and my advice to him (not that he ever took it).

I lost track of time.

Finally, after about 35 minutes I remembered I had this hair dissolving cream in the darkest recess of my body.

BLESSED MOTHER OF ALL THAT IS HOLY!

I sprinted to the bathroom and grabbed some tissues. I delicately wiped the cream from my nether regions and immediately felt the BURN. OH baby, BURN! It's a trick. It does

NOT burn while it's ON you. It BURNS as you wipe it OFF!

It was like hovering over a campfire. OOOOhhHHHH! It was like sliding down a sandpaper banister. I grabbed a washcloth and wet it with COLD water thinking that would feel better. It did until the air hit it again. OOOHHHH AAAAHHHHHH FUCK THE PEOPLE OF BRAZIL! Beads of sweat were popping up on my face. The heat was spreading. It seemed to take forever, but I'm sure it was only a few minutes as I carefully dabbed away the remainder of the kerosene. I grabbed my small mirror and with my foot up on the edge of the tub, body twisted like a gymnast, I looked. YES! I was smoother than the day I was born and twice as pink. I can't even imagine what a "real" Brazilian would feel like. At least I had the "dignity" of doing it in my own home in the privacy of my own bathroom.

That night I wore some loose jammie pants around the house. I walked like John Wayne. I sat down very carefully. I guess for those of you who aren't shy and who don't mind hot wax and ripping, the Brazilian in a salon is the way to go. For those of you who are thinking of flying the Brazilian Nairways, I have one suggestion: set a timer.

FRESH VEGETABLES

His frail, bony hands shook with Parkinson's as he opened his Christmas gift. Even before the wrapping paper was off, I could see he was smiling. Imagine being in a nursing home and nobody visited you, and yet, some stranger comes in with a few presents just for you at Christmastime.

Back in the 90's I was part of a program at work that obtained lists of people in the local nursing homes who never had visitors and became terribly depressed during the holidays. My fellow employees and I would buy a few items, wrap them, and deliver them to the nursing homes. We'd sit with our adopted elders and chat with them as they opened their gifts. You don't know the meaning of being humbled until you see an eighty-eight-year-old start crying tears of happiness over getting a bottle of Jergen's lotion. Anyway, this next story is a bit of wisdom given by a gentleman named Walter who was one of my gift recipients.

We sat close together so he could hear me, and I could help him with the wrapping paper. Walter's eyes kept getting a bit misty, and now and then he'd dab at them with his handkerchief exclaiming how the dry air in the nursing home really irritated his eyes. Hmmm. I agree, Walter. I found my eyes irritated and leaking too.

I smiled as Walter's thin hands reached into the gift box and pulled out a soft zip-up sweater. It was navy blue with a little wave pattern on it. The nursing home activities director told me Walter had served in the Navy, so I thought something that would remind him of the sea would be appreciated. Walter smiled and I could see he only had a few teeth in his mouth, but that was the best smile I'd seen in years. He wiped his eyes again (dry air) and started feeling the soft material then held it up to his cheek. His cloudy eyes closed, and he continued smiling while touching the sweater to his face. Then he opened his eyes and asked, "Can I put this on right now?"

"I don't see any reason why not!" I replied.

He was beyond delighted as I helped him shrug into his new garment. I helped him zip it up and he noticed the big zipper.

"That's going to be easy for me to handle. Those little zippers and buttons are worthless."

Walter wiggled around in his chair and sat up a little taller. Grinning from ear to ear he exclaimed, "This sweater was made for me." I agreed wholeheartedly.

I handed him another package. He looked at me with incredulous eyes. "ANOTHER GIFT? FOR ME?"

"Yes, Walter. I have four gifts for you. And I'll help you unwrap them if you're tired or you don't feel up to it."

That's when I saw a five-year-old child in his eyes. It was hilarious.

"I'm pretty sure I can open all of them. Watch me!"

I chuckled and watched him open his remaining gifts. Nothing too wild, but all genuinely appreciated.

There was a bottle of lotion with a nice, masculine scent. (You know, to combat all that dry air.) He also unwrapped a box of chocolate covered cherries.

"Thank God I'm not diabetic or they'd take these away from me. I haven't had chocolate covered cherries in decades. I'll ration myself on these." His eyes leaked a little more as he ate one . . . just one.

The last gift was a good-sized Teddy bear. It was wearing a sailor's cap and uniform. Walter stared at it. Just held it in his unsteady hands and stared at it. Then he brought it to his thin chest for a hug. If that bear's eyes had been real, they'd have popped out. I'm not sure if he was remembering his time in the service and how many friends he'd lost, or if he was just happy to have someone to hug and hold. I didn't ask. I was tickled he liked it.

I cleaned up the wrapping paper and boxes, then took a permanent marker and wrote his name and room number on his gifts. The activities director had a small table set up with coffee and tea on it for our little party with these chosen residents. There were only a dozen or so residents in this room, all assigned an "elf" to help them. I walked over to the table and poured two cups of coffee and went back to sit with Walter.

"You're a fresh vegetable." Walter informed me of this as soon as I sat down with our coffee. Uhhh . . . I'd been called a lot of things in my life, but never a fresh vegetable. This was a first. Walter could see the confusion on my face, and he gave a chuckle.

"Let me explain that."

"Please do, Walter, because I don't know if I should say thank you or leave."

He roared. "It's a compliment, honey. Definitely a compliment."

"Go ahead then. I'm all ears. I want to know why I'm a fresh vegetable."

Walter took a slow sip of his coffee, dug into the box of cherries for one more, and then began to educate me.

"This is the advice I gave my sons, nephews, and any other young man out there looking for a wife. I see too often these youngsters looking at the ladies and going silly over the ones who are too polished. They're all wrapped up in expensive clothes. They're covered in jewelry. And makeup. Oh my. What on earth are women thinking putting all that sludge on their faces every day? That can't be good for your skin. I've seen women with fingernails two inches long and painted in the ugliest colors. And to be honest, I have to wonder if anyone with hands like that knows what a real day's work is like? And how would you diaper a baby with talons like that?"

I nodded and let him go on. He was on a roll.

"You see, there's a difference between a well-groomed person and one who is just trying too hard. When you put more effort into covering the real you up, what are you showing the world? Fake. That's all. Just fake. Now, I'm not against a little bit of spiffing up, especially for a special occasion. But to wear so much paint on your face, and clothes that you're not comfortable in, and doing things just because everybody else is doing them? That just goes against your true nature. It's not right."

I thought about it. He was right. There were a few times when I dolled up and I admit I didn't feel like myself. Oh sure, I looked better than my normal, everyday self but, honestly, I didn't feel like ME. How did this old man know women so well?

"So, I tell young men to shop for a wife like you would food. And I don't mean that in any demeaning way. Just hear me out." He shifted in his chair and looked at me as serious as could be.

"When you go into a grocery store, have you ever noticed there are cucumbers, tomatoes, corn on the cob and all sorts of vegetables that are placed on those little trays then covered tight with plastic wrap?"

I nodded.

"So really, all you're seeing is one side of that tomato. You're only seeing what the grocer wants you to see. He's hoping you like the pretty part, but you can't see the bottom of the tomato that's gone soft and mushy. You can't smell it and realize it's not quite as fresh as you'd like. And you certainly can't hold it in your hand. The packaging hides all of that. It hides the flaws. It hides the real tomato. You really don't know what you're getting because you can't check it all out. You're being deceived, lied to. And after a while, you're just not happy with the choice you made."

I thought about this. He was right. Several times I'd picked up packaged fruits or vegetables only to get them home and a day or two later realize they were bruised, soggy, or even getting moldy where the packaging had been. I could put it together where he was going with this, but I asked him to continue.

"When you want something that's good for you, good for your health, will make you happy and strong, you want to examine it for yourself. You want to hold it up, turn it around, and see, smell, and feel what you're spending your time and money on. You want to get good value for your investment." Walter was tapping his finger on the arm of the chair with each point made.

"Always buy the fresh vegetables. Never go for the ones in the wrappers that are hiding the real thing. You want the real thing. Something that when you take it home, it'll last." And with that comment, he winked at me. He knew he'd gotten his point across to me because I was smiling.

"I'm a fresh vegetable." I proudly exclaimed. What a compliment!

Walter laughed and said, "Honey, you are a vegetable any man would be proud to have."

We finished our visit, and it was time to go. I hugged Walter and we both became a little misty-eyed. I asked him if I could come visit him again and he said yes, he thought he'd have the time for a visitor. I ended up visiting Walter several more times and learning more bits of wisdom with each visit. After a while his health declined even more and then he was gone. He was buried in his blue sweater with his sailor teddy bear tucked under his arm.

To this day, whenever I go into a grocery store, I look at the fresh produce. Then I walk by the packaged items and give a tsk-tsk on Walter's behalf.

FUNERAL LIES

"It's all lies." William stared straight ahead at the casket when the funeral was over and repeated himself. "It's all lies."

I didn't know what he meant, so I sat silently and waited to see if he'd give me an explanation. William was seated next to me in his dark blue suit that had seen its better days. His black shoes were well worn but comfortable looking. He was a little hunched over, but I guess at seventy-nine years of age that's to be expected. His fringe of a haircut circled his bald spot like a white fur stole on a woman's shoulders. Silence.

People were filing out of the funeral home saying their "I'm sorry" words of condolence to William's sister-in-law. Peggy stood stoically and nodded with sincere thanks to each person as they went on their way. Finally, the last person was gone, and Peggy came over and sat next to William. The funeral director and his assistant wheeled the casket containing Peggy's husband, William's brother, out of the room. Rodney would be cremated the next day.

Peggy looked at William. "Why can't they ever say what the person was really like?" The nuance of defeat clung to her bony shoulders. Sadness, sorrow, and emptiness were written all over her face, but there was something more. I pulled my chair forward and turned it around to face them.

"You've both said something about lies and some sort of deception. If I'm not being too rude, what do you mean by that?" I asked.

They both nodded at me, then at each other. William leaned forward and his arthritic hands gripped his knees as he spoke. "Rodney was my big brother. He was only four years older, but he acted like he was my boss from day one. It wasn't just sibling rivalry. He was mean, even as a child. He was by all counts a bully. Rod never pulled this stuff in front of our parents, so he got away with it for years. Even in high school he had a reputation for being an ass, but he covered it up by being a popular jock, so his actions were always excused."

Peggy's chin went up an inch as she chimed in. "Then I met him in college. I loved his drive, determination, and his total confidence. He was exciting, outgoing, and the typical big man on campus. I was in love with his image. Every now and then he'd say or do something a little off-color, but I thought I was just too sensitive."

I was getting an idea of how Rodney really was. I had worked with William's daughter for a little while, so I knew William from seeing him on several occasions. Coming to his brother's funeral was the least I could do to show my respect for his family. But you know me, I'm never one to pass up a story, especially from older people.

William spoke again. This time he repeated himself. "Lies. Do you know how hard it is to sit here and listen to the minister go on and on about what a good man my brother was? Rod didn't go to church. That minister didn't know him, but I suppose they all have their generic eulogies they can give to make the dead guy sound good. I suppose the truth would have been too brutal for the audience."

Peggy laughed a little bit. "Can you imagine if they told the truth? Can you hear a minister, priest, or rabbi standing in front of a crowd saying 'This guy was an abuser. This man cheated on his wife. This idiot was a drunk.'"

William chuckled and added to it, "How about 'Here's a lazy good-for-nothing who never worked a day in his life and sponged off everyone?'" Back and forth William and Peggy went, adding what I'd guessed were Rodney's less than stellar attributes.

I looked at their faces bathed in anger and had to agree

with them. I've been to many funerals. I can honestly say that at two, maybe three of them I was totally befuddled as to whom the clergy was referring with the "He was a good man . . . " speech. I remember looking around the funeral home or church and seeing faces with raised eyebrows. I wasn't the only one who was wondering if maybe a switch of caskets had been made and we were at the wrong funeral.

I didn't press William or Peggy for further details about Rodney. It was obvious from their attitudes and words and the very small audience in attendance that perhaps Rodney wasn't all that nice in real life.

That's when William looked at me, cleared his throat, and began to speak. I knew I was about to learn a valuable life lesson. I leaned forward so I wouldn't miss a word.

"I'm not saying I'm a good Christian," William started. "But I'm not saying I'm the worst, either. I try to do right by my family. I don't mind helping my neighbors. Volunteering down at the VFW or the Legion makes me feel good inside, and it's my duty as a former soldier to look after people. Being good to animals has always made me smile. Well, except for spiders. I guess that's a black mark against me but, damn, I really can't stand spiders." I stifled a laugh and let him go on.

"I have some advice for you, honey. Live your life right. You don't have to be perfect. Nobody is. But don't go out there and hurt people on purpose. Don't be selfish. Don't promise things you know you won't deliver. Don't break hearts. Don't use people for money, love, or anything else. Don't be an ass like Rodney." At this last piece of advice my lips broke open and a giggle squeaked out. "That's okay. It's true. He was an ass. And look how many people DIDN'T show up for his funeral."

Peggy was nodding her head up and down with everything he said. I can only imagine the nightmare her marriage to Rodney must have been. Back in the old days when you said,"I do," it meant forever. I'm pretty sure she had regrets about not escaping many years ago.

William wasn't done. "There's an old country-western

song and I can't remember the gal who sings it, but the gist of it goes something like this: I want to live my life so that when I die, the preacher won't have to lie." He let that sink in for a minute. "Apparently we're not the only ones who think a preacher shouldn't have to lie at someone's funeral. So, take this to heart. Listen. Not that you'll be in the audience, but when you do die, hopefully not for many years from now, do you want the preacher to tell the truth? Or do you want him to have to make up nice stories about you? Do you have the morals, the integrity, the honor of living your life the right way so there are no lies when you die?"

This was sinking into my brain. I'm no angel. I've done things I've regretted in my life. But I've also done things that weren't so awful. I wondered how the scales would balance. I'm not religious, so I don't necessarily believe in judgment day, but I do believe we answer for our worst moments eventually. I try to be a good person. I'd like to think I succeed most days, but I am human, and I know I fail at times.

As if to read my mind, William looked at me as I pondered his words. "Nobody can be good all the time, honey. But promise me you'll be as good as you can be from this day forward. It's never too late to do a little better than yesterday. Don't make the preacher lie."

The funeral director came back into the room and started putting chairs away. That was our cue to get out of there and let him finish his business. The three of us stood up and walked to the door. I turned and gave Peggy a hug. I asked her if she was going to be all right and, with a small smile, she told me she'd be better than ever. I hugged William. I thanked him for his words of wisdom and for enriching my life. I promised I'd do better than I did yesterday.

And every day I try to do just that.

ENVELOPES

I'm all for advancements in technology and how the world can run so much faster and more efficiently with the help of computers, cell phones, and all the other electronic gadgets we have today. We zing off texts, we tap out quick emails, click on the thumbs-up to like a post. We bank online and order goods from any of a zillion companies available to us. Next day shipping? On it! Communication is at warp speed and so sweet. We're addicted to instant gratification, whether it's for an object in our virtual shopping cart, or a reply to a question. No more waiting a few days for a reply when a simple "k" is considered a response to our inquiries.

Do you know what I miss? I miss the handwritten letter. I miss the special envelopes, addressed by a loved one's hand. I miss opening my mailbox, reaching inside and finding a short missive from someone near and dear to me. I love knowing someone thinks enough of me to sit down with pen and paper to let me know I'm thought of in a fond way. My mailbox is hungry for real, thoughtful, sentimental communication.

I remember talking to my mother about letters she wrote back in the 1940's and '50s. She used to write to her older brothers, Lee and Joe, while they were in the service. Servicemen lived for mail call and my mother knew that a letter from home, even one recounting the boring days of life in North Bangor, were cherished. I can only imagine the comfort her letters from home brought my uncles during those long, lonely days overseas.

It's my mother I must thank for my love of the written

word. She always encouraged her children to read from an early age. She herself was a prolific writer and I often wish I'd kept her diaries when she died, but she gave explicit instructions for us to burn them all upon her death. What a waste. I'm sure she had some interesting tales within the pages of those notebooks. It was my mother who encouraged me to write stories, poems, songs, or whatever entered my head. I worried about not being good enough and she'd laugh. "Not good enough for whom?" she'd ask. And she was right. I have numerous notebooks filled with accounts of events in my life, starting in high school all the way up to today. I laugh at some of the happenings I thought were important enough to log in my notebooks. In a way, I watched myself grow up through these journals and at times it's been hilarious and other times heartbreaking. One of the best lessons my mother taught me was to listen. She said the best stories are from people who have lived interesting lives and if you listen closely and ask the right questions, you'll be amazed at the knowledge they impart. That's why many of my stories aren't so much about me, but about other people and their wisdom.

Throughout the years I've written letters, but I confess email has made me lazy. I can still convey mushy sentiments in an email, but it's not the same as a real love letter. I send emails or messages via my laptop to my friends giving encouragement, praise, or comfort. Still, it's not the same as a handwritten letter lovingly placed in an envelope and mailed to their home. Technology is great, but not great for the soul.

My mission this year is to write more letters. I want people to feel the warmth and love that's implied with each envelope I address. I wish for the recipients to see that colored envelope in their mailbox, raise an eyebrow and ask, "Who's this from?" Then, fingers crossed, a smile will invade their lips and a full-blown grin will cover their face. Hopefully, they'll open the envelope, unfold the letter, and read my heartfelt words of love and friendship and know they truly mean the world to me.

Whether it's a letter to the love of your life, pouring out

your undying devotion or a note to a close companion and friend, each and every one will be appreciated. I have never been asked to stop writing letters from the people who have received them. Not once has anyone told me I'm cluttering their mailboxes.

I realize I'm a dinosaur and writing letters is a dying art; I plan to go kicking and screaming all the way.

SHANKS

"It weren't named after one of them there whittled knives you see in prison movies. Nope. Shanks has been around fer-ever and now it's prit-near jus' a mem'ry for the few people left from that area." Even after all this time in the North Country, Anna still had her West Virginia drawl and slang. Sometimes it took me a second or two to decipher what she was trying to say. Anna Godswick had so many stories to tell, and I was all ears. Let me share a couple with you.

Anna Frances Sayre was born in the hills of West Virginia in the tiny hamlet of Shanks. She was raised in poverty like everyone else during that era. Between the wars and the Great Depression ("I didn't see nothin' so great about it!" Anna exclaimed), there was rarely enough money or work for the people to get by on. Still, the people of Shanks and the surrounding areas survived by sheer determination and guts. Anna told me stories of her parents teaching her and her three younger siblings how to get by on very little. They ate anything made of fur and meat and foraged in the woods for edible plants in the spring and summer. "Ya don't get too proud when yer stomach's empty." Her remark reminded me of one of my former co-workers who never complained about food. He had apparently been raised in meager circumstances and he used to say, "Hunger makes a fine sauce." I'm guessing he'd have gotten along very well with Anna and her family.

Schooling consisted of Anna's mother Gina reading to her children from the well-worn family bible that had been passed down from her own mother. Momma would read each bible passage as it was written, then break it down to her native tongue of the local West Virginia dialect, which was probably more confusing than the bible itself. Anna said it wasn't until she was eighteen and working at a small general store in a nearby town that she picked up "talkin' better like real educated folk." Anna's father, Montgomery (known to his friends as "Gumry"), was a crack shot and taught his children to hunt and how to make any animal tasty in the stew pot. Between both parents, the Sayres had all the basic living skills covered.

It was at that store that Anna met Henry Godswick when she was almost nineteen years old. He was a fine young gentleman passing through on his way to northern New York. He had taken a few wrong turns and ended up at the general store to ask for directions. Just like those corny Hallmark movies, it was love at first sight for both of them. Henry delayed his trip for a few weeks and began courting Miss Sayre. Soon it was time for Henry to hit the road and head north. He promised to write to Anna every week. And he did. Eight months and many letters later, Henry returned to Shanks, West Virginia, and made Anna his wife. Anna said good-bye to her family and hopped into Henry's car for unknown territory. Anna had never been so far from home but enjoyed the changing scenery as her familiar mountains turned into flat spaces, then lakes, then back to mountains again. (Sidenote: Henry's great-grandfather changed his surname from some hard-to-pronounce Italian name to its rough translation–"Godswick"–meaning God gives us each a wick within ourselves to carry His light.)

"My first winter here was a hum-dinger, I tells ya!" Anna shook her head recalling how harsh our winters were compared to the much milder winters in Shanks. "We never knew ya'll could get BELOW zero on the thermometer! We mighta heard about it, but figgered it was in them igloos in Alaska!" Her slender fingers traced the small colorful beads in her necklace then she said, "The dang house was poppin'. I'd be sittin' in front of the wood stove and the sound of the nails poppin' would send me outta my skin. After the first winter I got used to it, but

I naddy wanna have to work outside when it's that cold!" Her skinny shoulders gave an involuntary shudder.

Over the following year or so I had several visits with Anna. She told me about her children and grandchildren. She spoke about losing her parents and two of her three siblings. Anna's younger brother still lived in West Virginia and enjoyed retirement from the local sheriff's office.

One day Anna looked extremely tired when I visited. I told her I could only stay a minute, but she knew I was just being polite. She was almost agitated, as if she really needed me to stay. "Ya know what's the best part of bein' old?" she asked me. Without waiting for my reply, she said, "It's the fact ya can say anythin' ya want and nobody argues with ya. They just figger yer old and squirrelly and ya got bats in yer belfry."

And that's true. Not many people will disagree with an older person who is obviously suffering from dementia or Alzheimer's. Just nod, talk about the old days, and let them ramble. "I got somethin' to tell ya and I'm not nuts. I've got all my noodles in one bowl, so don't ya think I'm a goner."

I held her hand firmly in mine and assured her I was positive she was NOT a goner.

"Back when I was just a smidgeon of a girl, maybe four or five years old, I used to explore the woods around our house in Shanks. It weren't nothin' unusual for me to go explorin' on my own. I knew if I got hungry I could eat the blueberries but to keep away from the green ones with the black dots on 'em. I played in the woods, swung on the vines, splashed in the little crick and amused myself. One day I was followin' that crick upstream and lost track of time. It was summertime, so daylight lasted awhile. Anyways, I was wading in the water and after a while I saw a little shack. I looked around and didn't see anyone, so I went closer. I know yer not s'posed to just go in other people's places, but this weren't no house. It weren't even a shack, really. It was just some logs and sticks piled against a fallen tree. Looked sorta like a branch cave to me. I hollered a "howdy" but nobody answered. Being a nosy kid, I went in and saw an old blanket on top of a pile of pine needles. There was an old hairbrush and some string. On the other side was two cups and a fryin' pan. I went back outside and saw a spoon hanging on a tree, along with some strings with shiny beads on them. As I was lookin' at the weird beads, I heard somethin' behind me. Turned out to be a lady. Funny thing was, she didn't scare me at all. She weren't creepy or ugly. The lady smiled and said hello and asked me if I wanted to stay a while. After walkin' all that way, I wanted a rest, so I nodded, and she pointed me to a log and I sat. She went inside her hut and picked up her fryin' pan and dipped it into the water. She started a fire in a little pit and put the pan of water on it to boil. Then she grabbed the two cups and put some flowers in them. She made us tea! I don't remember what kind of tea it was, but it was a pretty flower and it tasted almost like lemons. I told her my name was Anna and I lived downstream a ways. She said her name was Rosie Hasson and she was sorry she didn't have any food to offer. I said that's okay, I wasn't hungry. We had a good chat and after a spell it was time for me to go.

"I followed the crick back to familiar landmarks then made my way home. I told my folks about meeting a lady named Rosie up the hill and they both laughed and said it was nice that I made a new friend.

"I went to visit Rosie a handful of times that summer. Sometimes I'd take her a piece of bread or maybe a little bit of squirrel meat. She always thanked me fer it and tucked it inside her branch house. Never seen her eat a lick of what I brought her, but I figgered she was savin' it for later. Rosie taught me how to braid my hair. Momma always put it in a ponytail, but Rosie was the one who taught me how to braid it three dif'rent ways. Rosie taught me about dif'rent teas too. We'd go walkin' around the woods pickin' up the right flowers or takin' a little bark off special trees. Now and then we'd dig up some roots to soak and they'd be sweet as candy!

"It was gettin' a little cooler and the sun was settin' sooner, so my trips to see Rosie slowed down then stopped in the winter. I missed her, but thought I'd just pick up again in the spring when I could wander back up to her place and we'd rekindle our friendship." Anna looked out her window and stared off to a destination I couldn't see. We sat in silence for a few minutes.

"Yer prob'ly wonderin' why I'm tellin' you about Rosie. Well, here's the thing: Rosie weren't real. At least that's what my parents told me when I wanted to go see her that next spring. They told me there weren't no Rosie and that I was making it all up and they just went along with my story cuz it was funny. But I didn't make it up. I swear I met Rosie. We had tea. She taught me things." The pained look on Anna's face cut me. I knew she wasn't lying about meeting Rosie. At least in HER mind it was all very real. "My folks told me to stop with my story and not go back up the hill. I never did get to see Rosie again."

My heart ached for Anna. She'd made a good friend who taught her about wildflower teas and how to braid her hair. Rosie WAS real, no matter what Anna's parents thought.

"It weren't 'til I was growed up and almost eighteen when I saw some old newspapers tucked in the back of the general store in Shanks that I put it all together. Seems Rosie did exist. She was married to a man named Robbie and he weren't good to her. Beat her up a bunch of times, but back then they just told the woman to behave so's her husband din't need to whup on her. She went missin' one day and everyone figgerd Robbie finally went and done it. They knew he killed her. They searched for weeks and finally found Rosie's body buried out in the woods not far from their house."

I thought how horrible it must have been for Rosie to put up with that kind of treatment. Even worse, there were no agencies or programs for battered women back in those days. I surmised Rosie ran away to the woods and camped out there for however long she felt she needed to feel safe. That must have been when Anna met Rosie. But then Robbie must have found her, and his anger was the last thing she saw.

"Wanna know the best part?" Anna asked.

"Absolutely! You can't tell me all this then leave the best

part out of your story," I replied.

"I met Rosie when I was about four or five years old. That would have been back in 1927 or 1928. The old newspapers that I found in the general store that carried the stories about Robbie and Rosie were dated 1925."

I'm no whiz-bang at math, but I figured that one out pretty fast. My eyes grew big and the hair on my arms was standing straight up. A small shiver went up my spine. Before I could say anything, Anna smiled at me and said, "Now turn around and let me show you how I can do a double-braid in your hair."

GREATEST FEARS

Fears. We all have them. We've always had them. Like our tastes for different foods evolve over the years, our fears change too. When I was a small child, I had the common fear of the dark. As children, much of our world is understood by sight. Being thrust into darkness takes away the known and the comfortable feelings that we have come to expect in the light. It didn't matter how many times my parents would open a closet door or get down on all fours to show me nothing's under the bed. I knew in my heart there was something terrifying in the darkness of my bedroom at night time. Was it stories from my older siblings that made me fear the blanket of darkness? Or did I see too many movies that weren't appropriate for a youngster? It didn't matter. The fact was, I was afraid of the dark. As I grew older, shadowy places didn't cause me as much anxiety as they did in my early years. Perhaps it was all those nights of no monsters attacking me that finally convinced my mind that I was safe.

Fears can be natural or learned. I learned to fear snakes because of my mother's deathly aversion to the slithering creatures. If she saw a snake on the lawn, she'd shriek and run the other way. I remember the sheer terror on her face as her eyes bulged and her hands shook. She used to give us a quarter for every snake we killed. She wasn't tortured or tormented by snakes as a child, so I don't know how this fear originated in her. This was just a real fear that she carried and, therefore, I carry now. When a child sees an adult having a negative or scary reaction to an animal or a situation, there's a good chance it'll imprint on the kid. That's just nature. Animals will warn their young about dangerous predators. They'll teach their offspring to run, or to fight if necessary. Humans are much the same.

In my elementary school years, I was afraid of unknown situations. I was just a quiet, shy farm kid. We were always busy on the farm and didn't really socialize that much, so I wasn't used to crowds of unknown people. The first day of school was always agonizing for me. I would usually start crying, just tiny quivering pouts escaping my trembling lips. As I looked around the classroom full of strange children, I noticed a few others were in the same situation. I envied the happy, boisterous children who were smiling, giggling, and carrying on like they were in a new playground. After a few days in the new classroom, I'd calm down, make friends, and be just fine. Still, the dread was there every first day of school for several years.

By the time I reached junior high, I was fine. I knew most of the kids who would be in my homeroom, and I looked forward to seeing them after our short summer break. My fear morphed from the fear of the unknown to the fear of failing. My parents didn't whip us if we didn't get straight A's, but there was always a higher standard set for the three girls than for the three boys. Again, I believe this stems from one of my mother's deep-seated fears of being uneducated and not being able to support herself if anything should ever happen to my father. Back in the 1950's young women were expected to get married, have children, and run the household. Women didn't need to be educated beyond high school because they weren't expected to work outside the home. My parents had a rocky marriage at times, but they never divorced because they couldn't have supported two households. They stuck it out through thick and thin, but in the back of my mother's mind she knew she had to do better by her girls. She drilled it into our heads that we must succeed in school, so we'd never have to be dependent on a man. Ma encouraged us to study hard, learn new skills, and to be able to stand on our own two feet. Marriage was encouraged, but only if we really wanted it. However, she made it clear that getting married was NOT a "get out of work free" card. Ma let us know that we're responsible for ourselves and should never expect anyone else to support us. And she was right. It's not fair for anyone, man or woman, to expect someone else to foot the bill. If you're perfectly capable of working, then you work and contribute to the household, whether it's just you or you and a spouse. Back to my fears. My fear in high school was fear of disappointing my parents. I studied hard and earned good grades. I didn't drink, smoke, do drugs, or sleep around. I was a total nerd but that was okay. I had plenty of fellow nerd friends in my circle. I believe many of our parents had the same mindset for their daughters in that time period. The mothers wanted more for their daughters, so they pushed us to be strong and to work for whatever we desired. Nothing wrong with that and I thank my mother every day for instilling such independence in me.

Time passed and I entered the workforce. The usual fears of a new employee germinated deep inside me. Was I doing enough? Did I do my job right? Should I say yes to every overtime shift offered? What if I screw up? And yes, I did screw up, just like everyone else screws up at one time or another. Will I get fired? No. Will I do better next time? Absolutely. Fear teaches us to be better people. Having a healthy dose of fear is good, as long as you learn from it.

Was I afraid to jump off the Auckland Harbor bridge in New Zealand back in 2004? Damn straight I was. But I wasn't going to pass up a chance to bungee jump with a company that had a perfect safety record. I knew I wouldn't be in New Zealand again for a long time, if ever, so I pushed my fears aside and signed the waiver. It was the most exhilarating experience of my life! My eighteen-year-old niece jumped right after me. We were both on such an adrenaline rush for about three days and even now we still talk about our adventure. Totally worth it.

As I've gotten older, I've lost a few family members and numerous friends. Some to sickness, some to accidents. Fear of losing loved ones is the greatest fear of all. You can't skirt around this fear. You can't say, "Well, if I just go to enough funerals, I'll get used to them and they won't bother me anymore." That's not how death works. Death is too final. There aren't any do-overs. If you've watched people die, like I have with both of my parents, you'll know how hard those last few moments can be. All your emotions are raw and real. In your mind you're asking yourself what you can do to ease their suffering. And there's nothing you can do. You think of all the things you should have said, could have said, but now it's too late. The things you want to take back haunt you. Forever. This fear has a chokehold on you, and you can't shake it as you hold your loved one's hand and watch their life slip away. At that moment your mind is whirling like an emotional tornado. All you can do is pray that the person whose hand you're holding isn't feeling any of this wreckage. As I watched my parents gurgle and gasp their last breaths, I asked for them to be spared any more physical or mental pain. I'm not religious, but I'd like to think there's someone or something who helps ease us into the next realm. As afraid as I was in those moments, I was more afraid that my mother and father were suffering. I was afraid of being useless and not being able to help them. Logically speaking, I knew this was stupid on my part. Still, it goes through your mind as fear grips your heart.

Now that I'm considered a senior citizen (how did I get here SO fast?), I have some easier fears to face. Have I told people how much they mean to me? In another essay I address this concern. It bears repeating. I'd rather have someone tell me they care for me right now, rather than to wait until they're dead and just hear it from their survivors. "Yeah, Mom always said you were good to her." Not good enough. I want to hear it straight from the horse's mouth. And so do you. You deserve it. I've written letters and emails. One friend called me up and frantically asked if I was dying. She thought I was on my deathbed and was saying last-minute good-byes. I assured her I wasn't dying, but just wanted her to know she means the world to me. We had a good laugh out of that, but I know for a fact she still has that letter. She told me she reads it whenever she's having a bad day and needs to know someone appreciates her. Lump in throat. So yes, I write, email, call, or just tell people face-to-face that they matter to me. It's like giving flowers to someone while they're alive. Don't wait until they're dead. Give flowers, words, and love while you can. Don't ever fear telling someone that they have a special place in your heart.

People ask me if I fear my own death. I have a 50/50 answer on that question. I'm not afraid of what happens after I die. My own spiritual beliefs comfort me, and I hope my suspicions of the afterlife are true. What I do fear, however, is a slow, agonizing, painful death. I don't want to be trapped in a burning vehicle. I don't want to be sick and linger in a nursing home. That's my real fear–not dying fast. I know I can't fight genetics, so with my mother going at 65 from a stroke, and my father cashing it in at 82 after a battle with Alzheimer's, I figure it's a crap shoot for the next few years for me. I'm hoping to beat the odds. In the meantime, I'll take good care of myself, stop jumping off perfectly good bridges, and hope for the best.

SHOE THE TREES

If you have older folks in your life, you are blessed. They've lived through so much, have learned more than you'll ever know, and best of all, they have the most wonderous stories to tell. Make time to go sit with old people and ask about their youth. Have your friends and relatives tell you about how they grew up, what school was like, and if they fought in any wars. Question them about their loves, losses, and surprises. I enjoy chatting with my seniors because they always have such interesting things to say. Sometimes I laugh. Other times I cry. And then there are times when I'm just amused by their storytelling. Below I'll share a story gleaned from one of my seasoned friends. He was one of my favorite people and now I'm wishing I'd spent more time filling my notebooks with his memories.

My friend Harold was an elderly gentleman of 85. He had a few aches and pains, took three prescription medications, but overall was in pretty good health. His mind was sharp, and his wit even sharper. One day I drove over to his small but neatly kept house and went inside for what I knew would be yet another interesting visit. I walked in with a batch of my freshly baked yeast rolls (which he LOVED) and we sat at his oval kitchen table. We nibbled the butter-slathered rolls and sipped our strong, hot coffee from his U.S. Marines mugs. Harold was about 5'6" at this point in his life. From the pictures I'd seen, he used to be at least 5'9" but time and the real world have a way of shrinking all of us. Harold's light blue eyes squinted slightly behind his black framed glasses as he looked through one of his kitchen windows. He was staring at a tree, then turned back to me and cocked his white-tufted head to one side. My friend sat still in his grey and white flannel shirt and faded baggy jeans. I could tell he was in a storytelling mood but didn't hurry him. I was delighted to be his audience once again. Harold reached for a second roll with his slim fingers, tore it open, and dabbed a big glob of butter on it. He took a bite, winked at me and said, "Good thing I'm lean so I can eat all the goodies you bring!" He patted his flat stomach just below his birdcage chest. That's when he asked, "Are you superstitious? Do you believe in old legends and tales?"

I thought about it for a second and realized that yes, I am superstitious. I don't walk under ladders, I knock on wood for good luck, I never say, "Boy, it sure is a quiet night here at work!" and as often as I can, I say a prayer at 11:11. I'm sure I could list another dozen or so superstitions I observe, but to answer Harold's question, yes, I guess I am and confirmed that with him.

"Well, I used to live in Oklahoma as a young boy. We had some unusual beliefs and customs where I grew up. I bring this up because a story on the news last week prompted a memory and I thought you might like to hear about it."

I smiled and said, "Of course I want to hear about it. The weirder, the better!" I leaned in, all ears. I loved the faint twang Harold's voice still carried from his childhood in the Midwest. I smiled every time he said "memory" because when he said it, it came out "mem-ry."

Harold then went on to tell me that he'd watched a news item on television that was giving details about a young child who had gone missing in the next county. The family didn't realize the three-year-old could unlock their sliding glass door and exit the house. It didn't look like foul play was involved, but it wasn't ruled out. People are strange these days and bad people do exist. The little boy went missing and the police were called. They brought the dogs. They had search and rescue teams. They combed the nearby woods and fields near the family's home. Nothing. They scoured the river next to the home but no luck. The three-year-old boy hadn't been found yet and it had been over a week.

At this moment in Harold's story, he stared at his half-full coffee cup. He then lifted his chin and looked me in the eye and said with absolute certainty, "They should have shoed the trees."

I was at an absolute loss at that point. "Shoed the trees?" I asked. I'd never heard this expression but waited patiently for the explanation.

"Yes. Shoed the trees. Back in Oklahoma if a person went missing and the worst was suspected, the elders would go to the missing's home and take that person's shoes. They'd tie them to trees leading to the house so the person, usually a kid, would see his shoes and come home. It was to bring back the child, whether in the flesh, or in spirit. Too many times little kids wander off and end up dying out in the cold. Sometimes the searchers find their bodies, sometimes they don't. We believed a child would wander, forever lost for all eternity, if they didn't know their way back home. If they could find their shoes, they could find their way back. While it may not give the family back their loved one in the flesh, it'll give peace to the soul of the one who's missing."

Harold poured more hot coffee into his mug, added some heavy cream and stirred silently. Quietly he said, "I have a bad feeling this little boy is wandering on another level by now and won't find his way home. I hope they find him soon."

I agreed with him that after a week, things looked grim. There isn't usually a happy ending to stories like this and, sadly, by the next week that proved to be the case. It appeared the young boy slipped into the river and was carried downstream for several miles. His small, lifeless body was found by some kayakers on a sunny afternoon. His parents will forever be tormented and will always blame themselves for what was truly an accident.

As for me, I have to wonder about the shoes. It doesn't do any harm to tie some shoes to trees in the hope of leading the lost one back home, whether it's literally, figuratively, or dare I say spiritually? I hope to God I'm never in that situation and pray none of my friends ever are, but I can assure you that IF the unthinkable ever happens, I will be the first one to "shoe the trees" on behalf of the lost.

HEAVEN

Over the years I've bounced back and forth on the idea of Heaven and Hell. Do such places really exist after our bodies die? As a child I had questions. Many questions. Do we go flying up to the sky, float around on clouds, and have wings that allow us to flit here and there? Are we reunited with our family members who have gone before us? Do they look like they did when they were young or when they were really old? Do you age in Heaven? Would my grandparents who died before I was born know me? Is there food in Heaven? Do we even get hungry? Sleepy? What about going to the bathroom? Nobody had answers for this inquisitive kid.

Then I had questions about Hell. Do you have to be a bad person ALL the time to get a one-way ticket to the center of the earth that's filled with fire and lava? What if I swear now and then when I'm alone? If nobody hears me, does it count against me? What if I lied to my mother about brushing my teeth last night? How much bad stuff can I get away with and still go to Heaven? Where's the line that guarantees me a fast track to see the Devil? Do I get a warning shot? Even as a child I knew being good and perfect wasn't going to be easy. I was hoping for some sort of caution light that would tell me I'm dangling precariously close to the fiery gates of Hell and to straighten up and turn around. Still, no answers to my questions.

I've often wondered about other people and their ideas of Heaven and Hell. For a number of years now, I've asked this very question and have garnered a collection of answers. I find these interesting, touching, and comical. Like me, most people were young when they were introduced to the concept of Heaven and Hell by their parents or other adults. We all seem to have been given the same basic concept of both places when we were children. Funny thing is, the older we get, the more our visions of Heaven and Hell change.

I'll go first. My idea of Heaven is a place with no pain. No suffering. It's where I'll see my family and they'll be happy, fit, healthy, and totally at peace. They'll show me the ropes and tell me how it works. Yes, we look out for the people we left behind in our previous life, but we don't hover so much as to make them uncomfortable. We can't prevent bad times for them, but we can help them through whatever they're facing. We wait patiently for them to come to us in their own time. I hope to see every single pet I've ever owned. It's a fact that all dogs go to Heaven, so I'll have plenty of furry friends up there (except those damned ankle-biting Chihuahuas–the Devil has to have pets too). Although our spiritual bodies won't need food, there will still be coffee and chocolate in Heaven for our enjoyment. And I'd like to think if we have a soulmate, we'll end up together on this plane.

As far as Hell goes, I'm not as concerned about fire and brimstone and a red guy with a pitchfork torturing me for all eternity. I think life is hard enough for all of us. I can't think of one person who hasn't shed many tears over the years. We've all faced death, broken hearts, disappointments, sickness, and loss. Part of me thinks the "regular" folks have already paid their dues throughout their lives but just don't know it. Then there are others who are totally rotten from day one and were never productive members of society, never held human life in high regard, and were absolute menaces to the world. Okay, the Devil can have those people and if there's torture and suffering involved . . . so be it. That's my abridged version of the two afterlife destinations.

Dennis was 90 when I asked him what his vision of Heaven and Hell would be. "Heaven's easy. I'd be 22 again. I'd be just gettin' up in the mornin' and I'd smell the coffee Marlene had on the stove. Them buttermilk biscuits she used to make would be on the table. Best damned biscuits I ever did taste. I miss my Marlene something terrible. Anyway, we'd have our biscuits and coffee then we'd go set on the porch for a spell. When it got light enough, we'd load up our little wagon with a picnic lunch and fishin' poles and go to the pond. We'd fish all day. Then we'd come home, listen to the radio, maybe do a little slow dancin' in the kitchen. We'd have us some supper, sit on the porch again, then go to bed. That's my idea of Heaven. Me and Marlene." When I asked about Hell, he pointed to a picture of himself in a military uniform and lowered his voice just a little bit. "I've already been there. Not worried about it anymore."

Frank was 79 when I posed the question to him. "Heaven. Hmm . . . I guess that's where I wouldn't have arthritis anymore. And I wouldn't need these damned glasses either. I'd be alone up there because I'd want Barb to stay down here for a lot longer if she can. Same with our boys. Don't wanna see any of them until absolutely necessary. I'd have Remi for company. That was my old 'coon dog, named after my first rifle, a Remington. Damn, I loved that dog! I suppose my folks would be there, so it would be good to get caught up with them. As far as Hell goes, I think I've been a good man. I'm a Christian, but I haven't always been perfect. Hopefully God will forgive me and let me hang around and wait for everyone."

Hanna was 67 years old when I asked for her opinion. "Oh honey, that's an easy one. The Lord forgives us all, so Heaven is a wonderful place where we all meet again and sing, laugh, and rejoice! As far as Hell goes, I think there are only a few souls God can't save. And everyone knows you can't have Heaven without Hell, so the Devil takes care of the wicked people in this world." Hanna said all of this with such absolute conviction. I asked her if she'd been a nun and she roared. "No, but I did go to a Catholic school and college." Her faith was solid.

Ted was 51 years old and had to think about my question for a few minutes. "Well, I guess I sorta hope there's a Heaven. I mean, the thought of being happy and not having any worries would be nice. It would be cool to see my Grampa again. He's the one who taught me woodworking. He was good at it and every time I visited him, he'd teach me something new. I don't go to church, so I don't know if I'd have a place at the front of the line to get in," he chuckled. "But I'm not out robbing banks or beating my wife and kids, so I guess I'm not TOO bad of a person. Maybe they'll let me enter." I asked about Hell. "I suppose there's a place for the real assholes of this world, huh? I mean like the pedophiles, and people who hurt animals and such. Yeah, they can all rot in Hell. Am I bad for saying that?" I assured Ted there were no right or wrong answers. Just thoughts and opinions. I also had to let him know I agreed with his candidates for Hell.

That's just four of the many people I've asked so far. When I look back on my notes, I can see a few patterns in most answers. Most people do believe in a version of Heaven where you're reunited with your family and pets. They look forward to feeling joy, love, and peace. Most of the older people expect to meet Jesus or God and have all their questions answered. They were comforted knowing they'd be loved unconditionally in the Lord's house. The people who weren't quite so religious were hedging their bets on God and Jesus but had total faith they'd see their family members again. I guess meeting God and Jesus would be a bonus for them.

Not all, but several people worried about not being perfect enough. After our chat, a few folks felt like they still had time to set a few things right with the hopes of redemption. I like that theory. I suppose every day we're alive, we're given another chance to set things straight, do a good deed, or just be a good person. Nobody's perfect. We're only human and we all stumble now and then. I believe if we pick ourselves up, brush the dust off, and continue on, we'll be just fine. I'd like to think if you have a good heart and your intentions are sincere, then you have a pretty good chance of passing Go and collecting $200.

QUIET

Crunch. Crack. Snap.

I acknowledged the sounds of the twigs breaking beneath my feet as I slowly traipsed through the woods. I knew this property well as a child. It's been a longtime friend since 1974. Many afternoons were spent exploring and playing in this wooded area not far from the family farm. Forts were built. Trees were climbed. Swampy areas were inspected. I still remember the heady scent of pine needles and swamp grass, smelling almost sweet enough to taste. Pheasants and grouse would surprise me as I walked the main trail from the front lots into the wooded area. If you walked far enough on the trail, you'd come out in the back meadows which we hayed in the summertime. We reached those by tractor and wagons through the long, open stretch of hayfield near the house.

Sitting still was hard as a youngster, but with enough patience I could sit like a statue long enough to watch a deer or two come into view. The deer were creatures of habit. I'd often tuck myself behind a couple of trees not far from their main pathways so I could catch a glimpse of them as they wandered through the forest. At times I'd stifle my breathing so they wouldn't hear me, and most of the time I went undetected. Other times, I'm sure the beautiful beasts caught my human scent and that's what made them suddenly turn and dart in the other direction. I always appreciated their gentle grace, and yet understood they were food for our table too. My father was a busy farmer, but he had six children to feed, so venison was on the menu quite often. Being the "Jack of all trades, master of none," he cobbled together a sort of holster on his tractor for his deer rifle. There were times when Oscar would head out to cut corn or spread manure and we'd hear a POP! After a while we'd see him pull into the barnyard and invariably there would be a deer on the fender of the tractor or draped across whatever equipment he was using. He'd string the deer up and feel proud knowing he'd just put food on the table for his family again.

Time marches on. The folks sold the farm, then they passed away. The original farm has been sold a few times in the last number of years. I ended up buying some of the land that was near the farm, including the woods I remember so fondly. It's only 77 acres, but it's a peaceful place for me to go and walk around to collect my thoughts. I have a comfortable home about ten miles away, but I have no woods, no hayfields, no trails to roam. So, I drive ten miles, park my car, and get out to stretch my legs in the comfort and safety of my own territory. It's not just the serenity and natural beauty of this area that I love so much. It's a trip back in time for me whenever I walk through those trees and grassy meadows. It reminds me of the days when my family was close, everyone was laughing, working, and full of life. This was long before cell phones, video games, and computers. Everything was slower and it seemed my world had more meaning to it then. Right was right, wrong was wrong, and you were held accountable for your actions. If you wanted something, you had to earn it. You worked with your family and helped your neighbors. If you only had one piece of bread, you tore it in half and shared it. A simple life, but full of honest values.

When I wander through the fields and woods, I unload any troubles or worries I've amassed since my last visit. It's a moving therapy session. I guess I was into "forest bathing" before it was a thing. How could a person not be calmed and restored after walking through a quiet haven filled with friends standing tall and silent? That's how I've come to think of the trees. They are my friends and I need to visit them. I miss them at times. I often wonder if they miss me. When I enter the wooded area of my property, do the trees know I'm there? Do they have that instant happy feeling like I experience? Probably not, but it's a fun thing to imagine. We're all living things. We all have life pulsing through us. Energy thrums through our bodies, whether we're flesh and bone, or wood and sap. We live, we breathe, we grow. How many of us are like the trees I enjoy so much? How many of us cause others to smile, to relax, to be happy in our presence? The more I mosey through these limbed buddies of mine, the more I learn. They're teaching me to be quiet, to listen, to be present. I'm learning the value of silence, as I soak up all the quiet I can get amongst my bark-covered companions.

I hope I can continue my walks through this blessed landscape for many years to come. I realize the day will come when I'll no longer be able to put one foot in front of the other and visit my happy place. I take pictures and I hold memories in my head and heart. Hopefully that'll be enough for when my body doesn't cooperate with me and let me go there anymore.

These past few years I've been lucky enough to have a young friend who takes excellent care of my property for me. In exchange for all of his hard work, he and his sons hunt the land and bag a buck or two when they're lucky. I've already planned for him to get these 77 acres when my body decides it's had enough and ceases to breathe. We have an agreement that he'll spread my ashes in the woods, and I'll try to send the big 10-point bucks his way during hunting season. Fair deal, don't you think? It fills my heart with immeasurable happiness to know this land that has given me so much comfort and joy will be passed on to someone who appreciates it just as much as I do, if not more.

JUST IN CASE

As I write my short stories, essays, thoughts, or whatever you want to call them, I laugh at my attempt at tying up loose ends. I'm only 60 right now, but if you didn't know me, you'd swear I was 99 years old and cramming for my finals. I assure you, that's not the case. Maybe I have a touch of OCD and like things completed, finished, and neat. If that's the case, then there's definitely one letter I need to write. I really doubt the recipient will read this book, so he'll never see it. That's all right. This is a selfish book, for my own enjoyment and amusement. But just in case he ever does read my collection of thoughts...

Dear Love of My Life,

You didn't know that, did you? You had no idea I felt you were "The One" in my lifetime. I was mushy, told you how I felt, showed you in so many ways. I wear my heart on my sleeve, always have. In your mind you thought okay, we were together for a short time, we got along, but things didn't pan out, so we went our separate ways. That's true for the most part.

I'd like you to know I still think about you. I think about the connection we had. I obviously felt it deeper than you did and that's why you still wander through my head and my heart every day. You're the one that got away, as the saying goes. There are times when I sit back and smile over the silliness we shared. My mind remembers the inside jokes, the made-up expressions, and comical looks we shared. Nobody else has ever made me laugh the way you did. Our connection was more than just physical. It was cerebral and emotional. We matched on so many levels and it was pure enjoyment for both of us when we were together. I hope you'll always know how invested I was in seeing you happy. When your face lit up and you were smiling, that warmed my heart. I appreciate how your intelligence challenged me, and how your thoughts and opinions were very much in line with my own. We didn't agree on everything, but we had enough common ground to make our time together fulfilling. Even the thought of seeing you would put me in a good mood. I looked forward to spending time with you, whether it was a few minutes, or a few hours. Feeling your touch would send a buzz through my body, just as your voice would light up my soul. The effect you had on me was unmatched by any other.

Although we were never engaged, married, or made any legal commitment to each other, there was an unspoken understanding between us that maybe someday we'd be more than just lovers and friends. A few times we vaguely touched on what it would be like to share our future together. We never delved deeper into this possibility, probably because we'd both been hurt and used before. We still harbored the pain of past failed relationships. Not many people are ready to jump back into the fire. Totally understandable! We used that pain as safety nets to keep those talks about the future at bay.

We had our issues. Every couple does. We didn't see eye-to-eye on topics that were important to each of us, and that's why we derailed. Sad, but true. Still, I hope you know how much I appreciate the good parts of our short relationship and all I learned from being with you. Maybe I'm just being sentimental, but that's okay. You're a great man in so many ways. I will always respect and admire you for your multitude of positive attributes. Whether or not we've shared our lives with others since we parted doesn't matter. It doesn't take away what my heart still feels for you, and probably always will. I wish you nothing but happiness and fulfillment in your life, as I wish for myself.

"'Tis better to have loved and lost than never to have loved at all" - Alfred Lord Tennyson

BARN NINJA

You're never too old to be useful. Just because you're retired and can live life on your couch, should you? No.

Several years ago, I had cleaned and painted the inside of several barns for a guy I knew. I posted the "before" and "after" pictures online and received many comments. It's nice to be appreciated. One friend dubbed me "Barn Ninja" and jokingly said I could go visit her anytime and clean her barns. I thought about it then one day I messaged her and asked if she was serious. She said she was just joking . . . but IF I wanted to come and take a look at her barns, I'd be more than welcome to visit. And so, I did.

I knew Leigha Burkhalter when she was a bit younger, but at this time in our lives, she's a young bride and has a child. She works full-time at a local college and has enough irons in the fire to keep her busy. I stopped in one day just to visit and to take a look at her barns. Who knows? Maybe I could be useful. I certainly had the extra time, and there was no time limit on the job at hand. Leigha took me around her farm and showed me each barn and what she envisioned. I nodded at her every word. Her barns are old, but they're full of character. I could easily picture what each area would look like with a good sweeping and a little bit of organizing.

In Leigha's defense, she was not responsible for the condition of her barns. She'd bought the homestead a couple of years before and everything was "as is" for her. Growing up on a farm as I did, I realize farmers get busy and don't always have the time to take junk to the dump, or to pick up every string of baling

185

twine. Sometimes clutter piles up and, although the intention to get rid of it is always there, time doesn't always allow for it. There's always something more important and pressing to do on a farm.

Leigha has several horses, so her top priority was to make comfortable quarters for her handsome beasts. Her horses are living in better spaces than I ever lived in when I was in my 20's. They have bountiful grassy fields in the summer, and roomy barns for shelter in the winter. They lack for nothing. Those parts of her barns are perfect. It was mainly the upstairs lofts that needed attention, and that's where I came in.

After taking the tour of Leigha's estate, I told her I'd love to putter in her barns. I warned her that at my age I don't do a lot of heavy lifting. I told her I only have two speeds, and if she didn't like the first one, she sure as Hell wouldn't like the second. She roared and said she'd take any speed I have. I was anxious to get started because I could see all the hidden beauty in Leigha's old buildings. They have personality and charm. I wanted her and everyone else to see "the pretty" I knew was there.

A couple of days later I suited up in my jeans, old t-shirt, and work boots. (You never know where you'll find an errant nail sticking up.) I carefully tip-toed my way up to the loft above the main garage. The bright sun shone through the plexiglass-covered windows and highlighted a thick layer of old musty hay covering the floor. Pieces of broken machinery littered one corner of the loft. Old, dented buckets and lengths of frayed rope sat on the other side. A cracked garden hose lay in silence in the shadows. None of this discouraged me. I saw the magnificent space beneath this debris and I was determined to uncover it. I felt like an archeologist in anticipation of great discoveries.

It didn't take long before I began exhuming old hand tools that had obviously been used on the farm. They'd been set down and forgotten ages ago. I found saws, picks, yokes, and a number of odd wooden items that I'm sure went to wagons and other pieces of equipment. I set these treasures aside and hauled the junk downstairs. The old hay and straw were swept through a trap door down to where I could load it into carts to be hauled away. The loft was shaping up. One look at the hand tools and you could tell they were full of stories. The history in these implements is priceless. Leigha had given me permission to do whatever I wanted, but I'm not one to assume anything. I called her out to the barn, and when she had a few minutes, she came upstairs to a clean loft and dusty friend. She was tickled with the progress I'd made up there and loved the space even more than before. Not being TOO pushy, I asked Leigha if she'd like the tools I'd found to be hung up as a display. YES. She loved that idea, and that's where all those antiques rest now.

A week or two later, I went back to Leigha's and decided to attack what I call the "double loft" in her bigger barn. The upstairs in this barn has two big areas separated by a raised bridge-like platform. Sturdy hand-hewn wooden beams support the roof and walls. Wire cables had been strung across at some point in time for added strength. This was obviously the main haymow in the olden times. Two windows allowed sunlight in to dance on the dust I stirred into the air.

Again, the floors were covered in a thick, packed-down layer of old hay that really needed to go. I hated to be too needy or demanding, but there wasn't a chute to toss all the old hay down to the lower level of the barn, so Leigha's husband cut a hole in the floor for my convenience. (Thank you!) I donned my mask and gloves and went to work. I pitched hay and straw, swept chaff, dust, and dirt. I removed what pigeon droppings I could, thankful for my respirator the whole time. A few floorboards were loose, so the next day I showed up with my little toolkit. Nothing a few nails and screws can't fix. That double loft took a little more time, but it was totally worth it. I didn't find any treasures like in the first barn, no old tools or antiques. And yet the end product is enchanting. The wide-open loft with floorboards spaced slightly apart for ventilation makes your mind take a step back in time to when these grand old barns were built. Downstairs you can see where the addition and updating took place. The former owner did some cement work and I had to laugh when I saw his big handprint, the date, and his initials: PK. When I saw his initials, I knew I was in the right place. Coincidence? I think not.

The next barn I attacked was behind the house. Its loft is open, so it really didn't take long to sweep the debris out onto the ground in front of the main door. I bagged the garbage for the dump and tossed the old hay over the fence where the horses couldn't get to it. They're funny like that. Give them fresh hay and they'll turn up their noses. Pile nasty old stuff off in a corner, and that's where they'll start nosing around. Crazy. Anyway, it didn't take long to clean out that smaller barn. It could be used as a man cave, a large hunting perch, or a shed to store toys. The possibilities are endless.

The last building I gave my attention to was what Leigha calls her chicken coop. Although she has no chickens, it was obviously used as a hen house at one point. The previous owners must have used it as a catch-all after they were done raising chickens. I hauled the junk out, swept the building, and then neatly piled lumber and whatever else could be used on the farm in the future. That's one thing you learn early on–never throw out anything that could be used at a later date. Unfortunately, that's how junk piles happen. Still, it was easy enough to sort through the chicken coop and organize the useful materials and toss the rest away.

I have several points for why I'm telling you about Leigha's barns. I realize it sounds like I'm about to break an arm patting myself on the back. Gee. Aren't I wonderful? Don't you love me? Please excuse me for sounding so full of myself. I don't mean it that way. Here's what I'm hoping you take away from this essay: everyone can be useful. No matter what your age or your physical ability, you can help others. I didn't do any heavy lifting at Leigha's. If there was something I couldn't roll or tip, I told Leigha and she took care of it. I took my time. There was no deadline in getting these barns cleaned. It's not like they're entertaining the queen of England up there next week, so there was no pressure on me. I was doing something I enjoyed. I felt useful, needed, and wanted. Most of all, I felt appreciated. If you were to ask me who benefited more out of this barn cleaning task, I'd say it was a toss-up. The best part is that Leigha keeps these areas clean and tidy. She never wants me to feel used or unappreciated. And I don't.

And now to give credit where credit's due. Every cart I loaded with hay or horse seeds was unloaded by Leigha. I admit I'm not always comfortable running someone else's ATVs, so whenever I filled a cart or wagon, I had help with the other end of the job. Leigha was just as invested in this project as I was, if not more. Finding time between a full-time job, a baby, and running a household must have been tough for her, but she did it. And without whining once. I still pop in at Leigha's farm now and then, pitch a little horse pucky into the cart, and if I time it right, I get to ride one of her grand steeds. It's a win-win for both of us.

I know there are people out there who feel unappreciated, lonely, undervalued. I strongly suggest you find something you enjoy doing and find someone to aid and abet you in your endeavor. Don't be afraid to put it out there. If you have free time and you know someone who is struggling to juggle it all, offer a hand. They'll love you for it, and you'll make out even better in the end. I promise.

VARIOUS OBSERVATIONS

I've come up with a short list of observations I know to be true. Well, at least they are for me. I believe we all have our own truths. You may have experienced the same things I've listed below, or maybe a different flavor of the same situation. I think we're all basically similar in what life hands us and how we deal with whatever gets tossed our way.

1.   I don't trust people who don't like dogs. There. I said it. I will give a pass to the people who have been attacked or snapped at by dogs that weren't raised right. Those people are few and far between, but I totally understand if someone's been traumatized by a canine and therefore holds it against every mutt out there. The people I'm really pointing the finger at are the ones who turn up their noses and haughtily sneer, "I don't like dogs!" Most of the time they drag it out, so it sounds like DAWWWWWWGS, implying they're somehow beneath whale shit on the importance scale of life. Here's the interesting part: I'm firmly convinced dogs are better judges of human character than we'll ever be. Dogs are the most pure-hearted, loving, forgiving creatures on earth. However, if I see a dog walk away from someone, or won't go near a person, I trust it. I trust that animal's instincts. At first, I could see nothing wrong with certain people, but then once I got to know them a bit, I said AHA! That dog was right!

2. You're as happy as you decide to be. I'm not talking about running around with a fake smile on your face or playing Pollyanna and pretending your life is perfect. I'm looking at the bigger picture here. We've all been in situations that were less than ideal. Maybe we've had difficulties in our finances. Perhaps that romance didn't work out the way you had hoped. Your job could be a mind-numbing dead end, but you have bills to pay, so you slog through each week because you have to do it. We're only human and these emotional slaps sting. However, they don't have to define us. Self-pity is a slippery slope. You start with feeling sorry for yourself, then you gain momentum and anger jumps onboard. Before you know it, resentment has hitched a ride on your sadness toboggan. What kind of ride is that? Depressing. And unnecessary, too. When you acknowledge where you are, at the top of Poor Me Hill, don't lift your feet. Dig your heels in and stand up. Drop your hurt, anger, and frustration onto that sled and give it a kick down the hill without you. Every time you want to dip into the pouty barrel for a sip of whine, fling that ladle! Instead, reach for acknowledgement of the areas of your life that are going right. You have them. You've just lost sight of them. Do you have people who love you unconditionally? Are you healthy? Do you eat every day and then go to bed safely every night? Yeah, I thought so. You don't have it as bad as you think. It's okay to jump on the pity train for a short ride, but don't get too comfortable there. You'll find most people don't want to be around a sad sack. Smile, find your happy, and get on with life.

3. This one is mainly for the ladies, but it might apply to a couple of you men, too. The closer you get to the big event, the more pounds you will have piled on. Raise your hand if you've ever had this conversation in your head: "My co-worker's wedding is in a little over two months. If I lose two pounds each week, I'll be at least fifteen pounds lighter by then and will look like a supermodel in that blue dress." Three weeks go

by. New conversation: "Okay, I've been busy, but I still have time. If I buckle down, ramp up my exercise, eat more salads, I can definitely lose those fifteen pounds by the time the wedding rolls around." Six weeks brings another talk with oneself. "Damn it, I've been too stressed to really work on this, but if I dig in now, I can maybe lose ten pounds and that'll get me into the light green dress which isn't as pretty as the blue one, but it'll be alright just the same." The wedding day comes and you're standing there having this conversation with yourself: "Damn it. I'm up seven pounds, I look like a sausage, nothing fits right. I'm a failure." I see some raised hands out there. Happens every time, doesn't it? Yup. We need to forget about that big event and just take it day by day and see what happens. If you can only maintain where you are now, you've already won. Stop stressing about that date circled in red magic marker on your calendar. You'll be surprised at what happens when you drop that self-imposed burden.

4. Did you ever try TOO hard? I absolutely know this is a thing. I can bake cookies, cupcakes, cakes, pies, and a handful of other bad-for-you confections any ol' day of the week. And at the risk of sounding too full of myself, I'd say they were downright edible. However, if there's a special occasion and I want to take a treat, whether it's a dessert or a main dish, the Kitchen Gods will smite me. I think there's some unwritten rule in the World of Kitchen Gods that says if you're planning on taking something special to someone, then it must end up burned, flat, runny, or tasteless. If you manage to make it tasty and pretty, then you're going to drop it on the way to the car or you'll somehow trip before you get to your friend's front door and your container full of gorgeous goodness will be smeared across the front lawn. I'm probably exaggerating somewhat, but it SEEMS like this happens way too often. I'm sure it only happens occasionally, but it feels like the Humble Gods like to visit me on a regular basis. I've finally learned to under-promise and over-deliver. This way, I can say, "Sure, I'll bake a dozen cookies for next Thursday's

dinner." Then I whip up three dozen cookies and a batch of swirly cupcakes for good measure. Fate won't get me every time. I'm on to her dirty tricks.

5.   I may have hurt myself from doing too many eye rolls on this next one. Again, a show of hands if you've ever expressed interest in buying something, let's say a decent used car, and you put the word out there. You've posted it on Facebook, Twitter, Instagram. You've talked to all your friends and asked everyone to keep their eyes open for you. NOBODY comes forward, so you end up buying a used car from a stranger or a dealership. Your friends then see you driving around in this new (to you) car and THEN they say, "Why'd you buy that car? My cousin Joey had a much better car for a lot less money." "Oh man, I didn't think you were serious. I woulda sold you my Chevy instead of trading it in last week." "Wow, you paid way too much for that. My uncle owns a used car lot, and he could have given you a lot better deal." Yeah. We've all been there, right? Here's my word of advice to you: don't tell anyone what you're in the market for when you start the hunt. Do it all on your own. Buy whatever it is you want and don't tell anyone about it. When they finally see you with your new purchase, let them give you the "I coulda" comments. They're going to anyway, so the gist of this tidbit is to save yourself the trouble of putting the word out at the beginning.

6.   Have you ever had something special or important and you put it in a safe place and then forgot where that safe place was? We've all done this. Solid truth right there. I've decided to keep a treasure chest in my house. It's a cousin to the "thing drawer" or "junk drawer" we all have in our kitchens. That drawer is where old batteries go to die and leftover keys magically multiply. The treasure chest is different. It's not for valuables that belong in a fireproof safe. It holds envelopes that are labeled as to what keys are inside them. There are small plastic containers holding the spare parts that are hard to find for that gizmo I own. In my

treasure chest you'll find the special light bulbs that fit only that one instrument in the house. I keep tickets to special events in there. Anything I deem important goes into this chest. I keep an inventory list taped on the inside lid just to feel superior for a minute. When I take something out, use an item, or get rid of whatever, I cross it off the list. Now, whenever I want to lay my hands on something special, I just hit the chest first. Most of the time whatever I'm looking for is in there and I don't waste time rummaging through drawers and closets looking for my prize. Why didn't I think of this before? Because I was young, and I had a mind like a steel trap. HA! I could remember where I put everything. Those days are gone, and now my treasure chest is here.

This is just a sample of my own personal observations. I'm trying to find the humor in most things these days, and I think I'm succeeding with some of these endeavors. I find it liberating to be able to laugh at myself, and to not take everything as seriously as I once did. We may as well smile and see the upside of whatever situation we're in if possible. Makes the world a happier place.

FINAL HOUR

As I write this, the outside temperature is only 9°F above zero. That means I've been spending a little more quality time with Netflix these days. I don't hole up in my home ALL winter, just on those days that are painful to go outside. Retirement is fantastic. If I don't have to go outside, I don't. Love it.

Back to Netflix now. For some strange reason I've been gravitating toward some dark, yet oddly thought-provoking movies that make me think about life. And death. A few movies I've enjoyed lately have a common thread running through them: what would you do if you knew when you were going to die?

Would you go wild and start doing dangerous activities, knowing you're safe until "X" day? Or would you start "cramming for your finals" as my father used to say and get religion? Would you go out of your way to be kinder, more generous, more understanding of others? Or would you say every man for himself and go nuts?

I've had this conversation with friends over the years. The answers vary from one person to the next. I totally get the guy who has always played it safe who suddenly decides it's time to be a daredevil. He buys a crotch-rocket that'll go 140 mph and makes sure to verify that claim. I understand the woman who takes up bungee jumping. (Not that that's a bad thing, right Teri?) Or the guy who wants to go running with the bulls.

We're all faced with mortality. Everyone knows nobody gets out of this life alive, so we think about our endings and how we'd like to leave this big blue marble. And yet, we always think we'll have time to do all the things we want to do in this life. We delay. We plan. We save money for whatever it is we want to do. Then these plans get derailed. The furnace blows up, someone gets really sick, you're downsized and unemployed, or any other reason that puts the kibosh to your best laid plans. It's called life and being responsible. Unless you're a pseudo-star in a fake "reality" show, you really do need to have a job, earn money, and pay your own way in this world.

So, let's start small. Instead of panicking and freaking out over THE END, what if I proposed a one-hour time allowance? What if you were told you only have one hour to live? You won't be in any pain, you'll have your mind, you can speak, and your body can move the way you want it to move. What would you do in that hour? Would you go visit someone? Would you make a phone call? Or two? Would you take a pen to paper and write out as many things as possible for your loved ones to read after you're gone? The possibilities boggle my mind. When I play this one-hour game with myself, I find my answers change depending on the day.

Are there people to whom I should apologize? Certainly. Should I say "I love you" to anyone? Absolutely. Are there people I should forgive and let them know I harbor no ill will toward them anymore? You bet. If I know these things, why haven't I done them already? You know, just in case I don't get that one-hour heads-up. I think it's because I hold onto my deepest, most sensitive emotions too tightly. I'm afraid to be laughed at, turned away, or even ignored if I expose my feelings toward others. But I may have found a solution. One that might work for me, anyway.

For the past few months, I've started writing letters to certain people in my life. Selfishly speaking, I'm getting all those "I wish I had said . . . " thoughts on paper so I can clear my agenda at the end. I don't work well under pressure. I'd certainly need more than one hour to clear the slate, so these letters are getting written and will be dispersed upon my death. My goal, however, is to shred these letters one by one out of redundancy. I'd like to think that when the time is right, I'll have already expressed my love, apologies, forgiveness, and whatever else those letters contain, to the recipients.

Back to the original task. What would you do if you only had one hour before your ticket was punched?

At this moment in time, I think I'd spend it quietly by myself. I don't think I'd want any hysterical or depressing phone calls. No tear-filled good-byes. I don't believe I'd go visit anyone or send emails. I wouldn't even update my Facebook status to DEAD. I'd sit quietly in my comfy chair with a blanket on my lap, a hot cup of coffee in my hand, and be working my way through a bag of Hershey's kisses. I'd spend my last sixty minutes on this earth smiling and remembering all the love I've shared, all the happiness I've enjoyed, and any good I may have accomplished in my lifetime. I'd laugh at my numerous mistakes. I'd forgive myself for not being a better person when it was within my power. I'd cross my fingers and hope there is an afterlife and my mother, father, and two brothers (among others) will be there when I cross the finish line. When the final seconds count down to zero, I'll hope I've loved enough for a lifetime.

ABOUT THE AUTHOR

Pendra J. King

 Pendra J. King is a lifetime student of human interactions and has never outgrown the need to ask: "Why?" or "Then what happened?" She's always willing to listen to the stories of others hoping to glean some insight and knowledge which she can then share. Her own family's tales from when she was young have shaped her into the woman she is today, and she unashamedly admits her shortcomings as well as her strengths. Never one to learn a lesson the easy way, King offers the reader a chance to learn from her own experiences, which she colorfully describes in vivid and often hilarious detail. King is still a hopeless romantic in spite of her sometimes questionable or eyebrow-raising escapades into the world of love. King often insists on calling certain events "learning opportunities" instead of mistakes.

Made in United States
North Haven, CT
07 August 2022

22369181R00114